Si King & Dave Myers

THE HAIRY
DIETERS

BIG BOOK OF
DIETING 2

Si King & Dave Myers

THE HAIRY
DIETERS

BIG BOOK OF
DIETING 2

SEVEN DIALS

CONTENTS

It's now more than two years since we started getting ourselves into shape and keeping our weight under control. We never thought it would happen, but the weight loss has really changed our attitude to cooking. We still enjoy eating as much as ever but we're more clued up, more aware of what we're putting in our mouths. And what's most important is that this hasn't taken the fun away at all – we're cooking great food that tastes fantastic and doesn't pile back the pounds. That's why we've called this latest collection of recipes Good Eating.

Back when we started dieting we had a lot of weight to lose and, as you know, we did it. And for the most part we've kept it off and we're both determined never to get that heavy again. We weigh ourselves regularly, and if the scales do show we've slipped a bit, we know it's a lot easier to shed two kilos than twenty.

It's made us realise that healthy eating really can be good eating and we wanted to know more. When we made our *Hairy Dieters* television series we worked with dietician and nutrition expert Professor Ashley Adamson at the University of Newcastle, who was a fantastic help to us. We decided to go back to her and chat through some questions that puzzled us and perhaps you too. Here's what we found out.

Si: **We hear a lot about low-carb diets and low-fat diets. Is it safe to cut down on carbs and fat at the same time?**

Ashley: What really matters is the quality of the carbohydrates and fats you eat. More complex carbs, such as those high in fibre, are good for you. Fats such as monounsaturated and polyunsaturated fats are also good for you, but remember that **all** fat is high in calories. What you need to be thinking of is cutting out simple sugars (such as table sugar and fizzy drinks) as well as saturated or trans fats (lard, butter and the trans fats used in some ready-made cakes).

Foods high in simple sugars and saturated or trans fats are often low in nutrients but high in energy. They are what nutritionists often refer to as 'energy-dense' food. Energy-dense food is bad for you, compared to nutrient-dense foods (those containing vitamins and minerals), which are good for you. Examples of energy-dense foods are burgers, cakes, biscuits and confectionery. They give you few nutrients with a lot of energy (calories) in a small serving. Check the labels of some cakes and snacks and you will notice that although the portion might look small, the number of calories it contains can be surprising. Foods that are less processed or nearer to their natural form are less likely to be energy-dense. Nutrient-dense foods give you good value for your

calories – that is, a lot of nutrients – and generally include foods such as vegetables and fruits and wholegrain cereals. For instance, a 100-gram bag of green leafy salad might only be 30 calories but provides you with lots of vitamins and minerals – it's good for you and you can eat a lot of it.

Dave: People talk about good carbs and bad carbs but how do you know what's what? And what's the difference?

Ashley: Good carbs are complex carbohydrates that contain plenty of fibre – food such as whole grains, vegetables and pulses. The body absorbs these slowly, meaning it takes time to break them down and release the sugars slowly into your system. Bad or simple carbs contain refined sugars – think biscuits, jams, soft drinks, sweets. These are bad because your body absorbs them quickly, which creates sugar surges in your blood. The more your blood sugar levels go up and down, the more harmful it is for your body. Our body doesn't like the yo-yo effect caused by these foods.

Si: **Why is olive oil seen as better for you than lard, even though it contains as many calories? What are good fats and bad fats? And what are trans fats?**

Ashley: Olive oil is high in monounsaturated and polyunsaturated fats. Lard and butter are high in saturated fat, while some margarines and spreads contain trans fat and others are high in polyunsaturated or monounsaturated fats. Both saturated and trans fats are known to be bad for your heart because they can make your blood thick and more likely to clot. Monounsaturated and polyunsaturated fats, on the other hand, make your blood more fluid, meaning you are less likely to develop blood clots.

Our brain and nervous system are made mainly out of fat, which is why it is important to have some good fats, such as olive oil, in your diet. But it's important to remember that some oils are not designed for cooking. If you want to stir-fry your vegetables or roast them, opt for rapeseed oil or sunflower oil. Both these oils are high in monounsaturated fat and have a high burning point, which means they don't generate harmful substances if you overheat your pan. Olive oil is rich in polyunsaturated fats, which are good for your heart. However, it's best to reserve the use of extra virgin oil as a dressing for salads. It has a lower burning point than some other oils so might not be ideal for roasting or stir-frying.

Dave: **We know we should be watching our sugar intake but how can we cut down? What should we look out for when shopping?**

Ashley: When a food claims to be low-fat, beware – it may be high in sugar so check the ingredient list. Sucrose, maltose, dextrose, glucose, fructose, fruit sugar and ingredients such as honey, concentrated fruit juice and corn syrup are all just other names for added sugar. New guidelines recommend that no more than 5 per cent of our calories should come from added sugar. Given that most of us have about 14 per cent, that's a lot of sugar to cut out, but give it a go and you'll feel better for it.

Si: **Are sugar substitutes safe? Which are the best ones?**

Ashley: Artificial sweeteners and sweeteners such as aspartame, saccharin and stevia are all permitted and declared safe by the UK Food Standards Agency and the EU. They are lower in calories than sugar but using these sweeteners doesn't help you to kick the habit of eating sweet foods. It's far better to cut down on sweet stuff overall and have the occasional treat – you'll find the less you have the less you want. The more regulated your sugar level, the less likely you are to feel exhausted or down. Encourage children to drink water, milk or very dilute pure fruit juice instead of carbonated drinks, even if they are diet versions or sugar-free.

Dave: **What about the sugar in fruit and fruit juices? Is that OK?**

Ashley: Fruit and fruit juice contain vitamins and minerals as well as naturally occurring sugars so they're not as bad as sugary drinks like orange squash, cola and lemonade. Those are basically sugar and water with a few flavourings. But remember that pure fruit juice contains a similar amount of sugar to non-diet drinks, such as colas, so if you're drinking juice regularly you can end up taking in too many calories in the form of sugar. It's better to eat whole fruit as it is and drink plain water or other beverages such as tea, herbal or fruit teas, or milk (ideally, 1 per cent-fat milk) to keep your body hydrated.

In general, we find it easier to take calories as liquids rather than solids. Our stomach also digests liquids quicker, meaning that you might end up drinking more (so taking in more calories) and being hungry quicker when consuming liquids compared to solid food.

Si: **Is brown bread better for us than white sliced and why?**

Ashley: This is an interesting question, as people often confuse wholemeal bread with brown bread, some of which is simply white flour dyed with caramel to add colour. It's wholemeal bread – bread with bits in – that we should generally eat, as it is high in fibre and contains a variety of vitamins and minerals. If you really don't like wholemeal bread, the next best are the newer half and half breads. As before when we talked about avoiding energy-dense foods, there's a concept in nutrition called 'nutrient density'. In general, foods that provide more nutrients for the same amount of calories are described as nutrient-dense and considered healthiest, as they help us avoid consuming empty calories. So the next time you eat something ask yourself: what does this food give me other than calories? As a rough guide, if it provides lots of important minerals or vitamins you know that it is probably good for you.

Dave: **I love salt. I know it's bad for my heart and blood pressure but will eating salty foods affect my weight?**

Ashley: Many salty foods, such as crisps and peanuts, are also high in fat so contain lots of calories – they're energy-dense – so it's best to limit your intake. In cooking, try using less salt or none at all and use lovely herbs and spices for flavour instead – I know you do this in lots of your recipes. Try covering up some of the holes on your salt shaker so you don't put so much on your food. You will be surprised that your taste buds will get used to less salt – really.

Si: **How much water should I drink every day?**

Ashley: The European Food Safety Authority advises that women should drink about 1.6 litres of fluid and men about 2.0 litres of fluid per day. That's equivalent to eight 200ml glasses for a woman and ten 200ml glasses for a man. This could be in the form of tea, herbal/fruit teas, coffee, milk (semi-skimmed or 1 per cent-fat milk) or the occasional fruit juice.

Dave: **What about exercise for weight loss? How many tangos do I need to do to work off a bag of crisps or a chocolate bar?**

Ashley: The current recommendation for adults is 30 minutes of moderate physical activity at least five times a week. When you think of it in terms of food, one standard Mars bar = 50 minutes of aqua aerobics, while just three minutes of dancing burns off the calories in a carrot, and 16 minutes of walking = one banana.

Some people have intense gym workouts on a couple of days, then think it's fine to spend the rest of the time lying on the sofa watching television. This is what some scientists refer to as being an 'active couch potato'. It's best to distribute exercise through the day and be less sedentary if you want to reduce your risk of developing diabetes or high blood pressure. If you're working in an office, take a short break every hour to stretch or walk down to the water cooler. Walking is good exercise and free. Why drive to the gym when you can walk to work or the shops?

Si: **Can we eat our five a day and still lose weight?**

Ashley: If you snack on fruit and veg and include plenty in your main meals, you'll have less room for unhealthy snacks such as crisps, cakes and pies in your diet, so that's good for weight control.

Fruit and vegetables are generally lower in calories than foods such as dairy products, meats and cereals. When selecting your fruit and vegetables, choose some with a high water content, such as berries, watermelons, pineapples, cucumbers, green leafy vegetables, and tomatoes. These are generally rich in vitamins but low in calories – that is, they have a low energy density but high nutrient density. This means you are more likely to get all the vitamins and minerals you need in fewer calories so encouraging weight loss.

Dave: Will I lose more weight if I eat more fibre and go to the loo more often?

Ashley: Some types of fibre help your body get rid of some fat (cholesterol) and gets it out of your system. More importantly, fibre helps you feel full for longer and keeps those hunger pangs at bay. Foods high in fibre tend to be complex carbohydrates and so take longer for your body to digest and avoid that yo-you effect. It doesn't necessarily mean you'll be spending all your time in the toilet, though. It just helps improve your digestive system so you don't get constipated (no fun for anyone) and have more regular bowel movements.

Si: Sometimes I don't feel like eating breakfast but should I have some anyway? Is it true that you need to eat something in the morning to get your metabolism going?

Ashley: People with high levels of stress hormones and insulin resistance tend to have a lower appetite in the morning and want to eat more later in the day. Because eating later in the day is related to weight gain, continuing this pattern of eating will create a continuous cycle wherein you increase your body's stress hormones, which makes you want to skip breakfast and eat later in the day. This in turn increases your stress hormones and so on. Think of your body as a clock. From time to time, our body clock goes off track and we need to reset it in order to allow our metabolism to function better. If you encourage yourself to have breakfast every day, even if it's just a light snack or a piece of fresh fruit, then over time you will notice that your metabolism will reset itself and you'll start craving more food in the morning and less in the evening.

Dave: **I've heard people talk about visceral fat. What is this and can thin people have it?**

Ashley: Visceral fat is belly fat – the fat we put on round our waists and our organs (inside fat). There's good evidence that the larger our waistlines the higher our risk of conditions such as heart disease and cancers. This is why keeping a check on our waist measurement as well as our body weight is important. As a general rule, in men a waist measurement of more than 102cm is considered to be unhealthy, while in women a waist measurement above 88cm is likely to be linked with health problems. The different cut-offs are related to the fact that men are more likely to have an apple shape and gain weight easily around the abdomen, while women are more likely to have a pear shape, and gain weight around the hips. Just another of our many differences! If your waist measurement is above these numbers your health could be at risk. Your waist measurement is easy to keep track of too – we all know when we've had to move to the next notch on our belts or those trousers seem to have 'shrunk in the wash'!

Si: **When you look at a food packet there are usually two measurements for calories. One is more than the other, so which should we be looking at?**

Ashley: Both measure the amount of energy we are putting in our bodies but they are different units (like inches and centimetres). Kj (kilojoules) are equal to just over four times kcal (kilocalories – sometimes called just calories). Checking your kcal is easier because we often hear nutritional recommendations in calories.

It's difficult to give precise calorie recommendations because we are all different sizes and have varying levels of activity. Think of types of cars – some are minis, others are big four-wheel drives. Neither uses much petrol just to idle at the roadside but they need different amounts of petrol to drive 50 miles. In the UK, on average, men are recommended to have a maximum of about 2,500 kcal and women 2,000 kcal, though this varies depending on body size and activity levels (how many calories you burn). Remember, though, this is a guide, not a goal.

Keep in mind that some food labels show only a rough estimate of the calories they contain, so the bowl of cereal or muffin you're eating might have a few more calories than you think. Also remember to check the serving size. You might think the calorie count is for a whole packet but it could be for only a portion of it. If you want to lose weight, then you need to eat less than your body uses (burns). As a rough guide, if your weight is currently stable and you eat about 500 calories less each day for a week you'll lose about 500 grams a week or a kilo in two weeks.

QUICK TIPS

We've given calorie counts (in kilocalories) for all our recipes so follow the recipes carefully so you don't change the calorie count. Weigh your ingredients and use proper spoons and a measuring jug. We always say how many people the recipe will serve, so u don't eat more than your fair share!

We mention spray oil in quite a few of the recipes, as this is an easy way of reducing the amount of oil you use. Buy the most natural kind you can find and spritz it lightly. If you don't want to use spray oil, just brush on a small amount of oil.

Peel onions and garlic unless otherwise specified. Use fresh stock or stock made with a cube, as you prefer. And we use free-range eggs and chicken whenever possible. We've also highlighted recipes suitable for freezing. Follow the usual safety advice when defrosting and reheating.

- Don't skip breakfast. You'll only be tempted to stuff yourself mid-morning.

- Eat slowly. Don't gobble your food – chew it well, put your fork down between bites and take your time. Relish every mouthful.

- Before you eat something, ask yourself if you really are hungry. Try having a glass of water – sometimes you're just thirsty, not hungry at all. When you fancy a treat, go sparkling.

- Carry a healthy snack with you when you're out and about. That way you won't be tempted to grab choc bars and crisps. And try taking a flask of soup or a box of home-made salad to work with you for lunch. That way you know exactly what you're eating.

- Don't go shopping for food when you're hungry. You'll be tempted to buy stuff you know you shouldn't be eating.

- Drink water, not sweet fizzy drinks – they're packed with calories. And even innocent-looking drinks like fresh juices and smoothies are high calorie and best avoided. Cut down on alcohol too.

- Use smaller plates and take smaller portions. We were always generous with our helpings before, but now we stick to sensible portions. Don't guess – use your kitchen scales.

- Trim visible fat off meat, or buy leaner cuts. Loin means lean. Belly pork is great but not for your belly.

- If you do fancy some French bread, take out some of the stodge and just enjoy the crunchy crust. This goes for bread rolls too.

- When you feel like you want another helping, wait 20 minutes. It takes that long for the message that you're full to get through to your brain and you'll probably find you don't need any more food after all.

- Look out for hidden sugar in foods such as ready meals and fruity yoghurts. It's surprising how much there is and it ups the calorie count.

- Weigh yourself regularly but be prepared for little variations. Some people like to get on the scales every day, while others prefer once or twice a week, but the important thing is to keep a check on yourself.

- Don't pick as you cook. Dave's mam said, "Folks who are pickers need bigger knickers!"

FEEDING FRIENDS

When you've got friends and family coming round it's tempting to have a night off the diet, but with our recipes there's no need. You can make a delicious meal without breaking your calorie limits, allowing you to stick to your diet and do your guests' waistlines a favour too. Don't tell them that the food is low calorie. They'll never guess and they'll just think you're an amazingly talented cook!

Here are couple of ideas for menus from this book:

MENU 1

Wild mushroom soup
(74 calories per serving)

Fish Véronique
(231 calories per serving)

Raspberry and
orange soufflés
(105 calories per serving)

Add some veg or salad and
you have a three-course meal
for around 500 calories

MENU 2

Spicy mussels
(160 calories per serving)

Pork and black
bean stew
(380 calories per serving)

Instant sorbet
(87 calories per serving)

Three really great courses for
just over 600 calories

MENU 3

And if you feel like treating
yourself to one of our more
lavish puds, go for a low-cal
main course first:

Mediterranean fish soup
(220 calories per serving)

Quick rice pudding
with marsala sauce
(341 calories per serving)

A FEW LITTLE NOTES FROM US

- We've given calorie counts for our dishes so follow the recipe carefully so you don't change the count. Weigh ingredients and use proper spoons and a measuring jug. We always say how many people a recipe serves, so you don't eat more than your share.

- We mention spray oil in quite a few recipes, as this is an easy way of reducing the amount of oil you use. Buy the most natural kind you can find and spritz it lightly. If you don't want to use spray oil, just brush on a small amount of oil with a pastry brush.

- Peel onions, garlic and all other vegetables and fruit unless otherwise specified.

- Use free-range eggs and free-range chicken whenever possible. Whatever you're cooking, it always pays to buy the best and freshest seasonal ingredients you can afford. We reckon that 95 per cent of good cooking is good shopping – great ingredients need less fussing with.

- If you're really organised you might have some of your own home-made stock in your freezer. Otherwise, it's fine to use the fresh stocks available in the supermarkets or buy cubes or the little stockpots. Many are pretty good these days.

BREAKFAST AND BRUNCH

We're much more adventurous with our breakfasts now than we used to be. We still love our eggs, but instead of a fry-up we might go for a delicious frittata-style omelette stuffed with fresh veg, or some little pots of baked eggs with different fillings. When time is short, we both love a smoothie, which gives you loads of goodness in a matter of minutes and really keeps you going. And for a special treat, try our fab ham, corn and chilli muffins. They're awesome!

AMERICAN-STYLE FLUFFY PANCAKES

135 calories per portion (3 pancakes)

These little morning lovelies are usually made with ricotta but we use quark. This is nought to do with ducks but is a low-fat dairy product available in most supermarkets, which takes the calorie count of the pancakes right down. Enjoy them with some low-fat yoghurt or crème fraiche and some extra berries. You can also drizzle on a little maple syrup – a teaspoonful only adds about 15 calories. We're sure you won't need any encouragement, but eat these as soon as they're cooked to enjoy them at their very best.

Serves 4 (3 pancakes each)
Prep: 10 minutes
Cooking time: 12 minutes

100g plain flour
1 tsp baking powder
50g quark
125g semi-skimmed milk
2 egg whites
100g blueberries
oil, for spraying

Sift the flour and baking powder into a large bowl. In a separate bowl, mix the quark and milk until fairly smooth. Add a little of the quark mixture to the flour to make a fairly thick paste, then use an electric mixer to gradually incorporate the rest.

In a clean bowl, whisk the egg whites until they form dry, stiff peaks. Using a metal spoon, fold 2 tablespoons of the egg whites into the batter to loosen it a little. Gently fold in the rest, being careful not to knock the air out of the mixture. Stir the blueberries into the batter.

Heat a large non-stick frying pan over a medium heat, then give it one quick spray of oil. Dollop large spoonfuls of the batter into the frying pan – you should be able to cook at least 3 at once. When you see lots of little air bubbles breaking through on the surface of the pancakes and the batter is starting to look as though it is setting, flip each one over and cook for another minute. Remove and set aside to keep warm.

Continue to cook the rest of the pancakes in the same way, then serve immediately.

BUCKWHEAT PANCAKES

75 calories per pancake; 193 calories with filling

Buckwheat flour makes great pancakes – known as galettes to our friends in Brittany – and it's available in most supermarkets. Despite the name, it's not actually a wheat and it's gluten free so is good for those with wheat allergies. The batter uses one egg and makes eight pancakes – more than you need – but it freezes well or can be kept in the fridge for a few days.

Serves 4
Prep: 15 minutes, plus an hour standing time for the batter if possible
Cooking time: 15 minutes

Pancakes
100g buckwheat flour
1 pinch of salt
1 large egg
300ml semi-skimmed milk
oil, for spraying

Filling
1 tbsp olive oil
100g mushrooms, wiped clean and thinly sliced
1 garlic clove, finely chopped
1 tbsp finely chopped fresh parsley
4 eggs
flaked sea salt
freshly ground black pepper

FREEZE!

Pour any batter you don't use into an airtight plastic container and freeze for another time.

Sift the flour into a bowl and stir in the salt. Make a well in the flour and break in the egg, then gradually incorporate the flour into the egg until you have a thick paste. Start mixing in the milk, little by little, until you have a smooth batter. If you have time, leave the batter to stand for about an hour, but don't worry if you can't.

To make the filling, heat the oil in a non-stick frying pan and add the mushrooms. Fry until they are tender, then add the garlic and parsley. Season and cook for another minute or two, then tip everything into a bowl. Set the pan aside for cooking the eggs later.

To make the pancakes, heat a small non-stick frying pan over a medium heat and spritz lightly with oil. Hold the pan in one hand and add a small ladleful of batter (about 2 tablespoons), swirling quickly so the entire base of the pan is coated. Cook the pancake on one side until lots of little air bubbles appear and a palette knife slides easily under it. Flip the pancake over and cook on the other side for about half a minute, then slide on to a plate. Make 3 more pancakes in the same way. You shouldn't need to add more oil to the pan – the remaining pancakes will brown more quickly, but just turn down the heat a little and keep a close eye on them.

Break the eggs into the pan you used to cook the mushrooms and fry gently until the whites are set and the yolks are still runny.

Return a pancake to the pancake pan. Put a quarter of the mushrooms in the centre and top with a fried egg. Turn the edges of the pancake into the centre – they won't meet so you'll see the filling peeking through the gap. Transfer to a warm plate. Fill the rest of the pancakes in the same way and serve immediately.

VEGETABLE FRITTATA

230 calories per portion

A frittata is basically a good hearty omelette that's finished off under the grill. We like to roast most of the veg for extra flavour and you can cook them the night before if you want a quick brunch dish for the morning. This dish is excellent cold too, so good for a lunch box or picnic basket. Vary the veg according to your taste and the season – asparagus, peas, mushrooms are all good – but stay way from the spuds and keep your calorie count in mind.

Serves 4
Prep: 15 minutes
Cooking time: 40 minutes

2 red onions, cut into wedges
1 courgette, cut into rounds
1 red pepper, deseeded and sliced
   lengthways into strips
200g butternut squash,
   peeled and diced
1 tbsp olive oil
1 tsp dried oregano
½ head of broccoli, broken into
   small florets
50g green beans, cut in half
6 eggs
oil, for spraying
6 cherry tomatoes, halved
handful of fresh basil leaves,
   torn
flaked sea salt
freshly ground black pepper

First roast the veg. Preheat the oven to 200°C/Fan 180°C/Gas 6. Line a baking tray or roasting dish with non-stick baking paper and spread the onions, courgette, red pepper and butternut squash over it. Drizzle on the olive oil, then turn the vegetables over with your hands, making sure they are all lightly coated with oil. Sprinkle with the oregano. Place the baking tray in the oven and roast the vegetables for 30 minutes, then set aside.

Bring a small saucepan of water to the boil and blanch the broccoli and beans for 2 minutes, then drain. Crack the eggs into a bowl, beat them with a fork and season with salt and pepper.

Heat your grill to its highest setting. Lightly spray a large non-stick frying pan with oil and place the pan over a medium heat. Tip the roasted veg into the frying pan and spread them out as evenly as you can so that each quarter gets a good balance of the different vegetables. Add the broccoli, green beans and cherry tomatoes and sprinkle over the torn basil.

Pour the eggs over the vegetables. Cook over a medium heat until the base of the frittata has set – you'll see the edges starting to turn brown. Place the frying pan under the hot grill and cook for a few more minutes until the eggs have set and the top of the frittata has started to puff up slightly. Remove carefully – the handle of the pan will be hot – cut into quarters and serve.

BAKED EGGS

155 calories per portion (with mushroom filling); 187 calories (with chorizo)

These make a really special breakfast or brunch with one of our fab fillings. We love chorizo and although it's high in calories, lots of the calorific oil comes out when you fry it. It's mega tasty too, so you don't need a lot.

Serves 4
Prep: 10 minutes
Cooking time: 15–20 minutes

oil, for spraying
4 large eggs
4 tsp finely grated Cheddar,
   Gruyère or other hard cheese
flaked sea salt
freshly ground black pepper

Mushroom filling
1 tbsp olive oil
4 button mushrooms, wiped and
   finely sliced
1 garlic clove, finely chopped
4 squares of frozen spinach,
   defrosted and liquid squeezed out
a grating of nutmeg

Chorizo filling
50g chorizo, finely chopped
½ red pepper, deseeded and
   finely chopped
½ onion, finely chopped
1 garlic clove, finely chopped
4 tomatoes, roughly chopped
basil leaves, shredded

Preheat the oven to 190°C/Fan 170°C/Gas 5. Very lightly mist 4 ramekins with oil. Choose your filling and prepare as below, then divide the filling between the ramekins. Break an egg into each ramekin, on top of the filling, and season with salt and pepper. Sprinkle a teaspoon of cheese over each egg and cover each ramekin with foil.

Put the ramekins in a roasting or baking dish and pour in hot water to come about two-thirds up the sides of the ramekins. Bake in the oven for up to 15 minutes, checking them after 10 minutes. You can cook the eggs to your liking, but after about 10 minutes the whites should be set and the yolks should still be runny.

Mushroom filling
Heat the olive oil in a frying pan, add the mushrooms and cook them until soft. Add the garlic and season with salt and pepper, then cook for another minute. Make sure the spinach is as dry as possible before adding it to the mushrooms in the pan. Grate over a little nutmeg and stir well to combine.

Chorizo filling
Put the chorizo in a frying pan and fry until brown – you don't need to add any extra oil, as the chorizo will immediately start giving out its own. Remove the chorizo and place it on some kitchen paper to drain, making sure there's only a very small amount of oil left in the frying pan. Add the red pepper and onion, then sauté until soft. Add the garlic and fry for another minute, then add the tomatoes. Cook for a few minutes until the tomatoes have reduced down slightly, then tip the chorizo back into the pan and stir in the basil.

SMOOTHIES

70–104 calories per serving

Smoothies make a perfect breakfast treat or a quick pick-me-up at any time of day. We know we need fibre in our diet but sometimes it's nice to have a bit of smooth with the rough! It's so easy to make your own smoothies – some of the ready-made versions are expensive and can be full of calories.

Serves 2
Prep: 5–10 minutes

Green smoothie
50g spinach
1 celery stick
1 apple
juice of 1 orange
juice of 1 lime
½ tsp grated fresh root ginger
handful of ice cubes

Banana, strawberry and
blueberry smoothie
1 banana
100g strawberries
100g blueberries
50ml low-fat natural yoghurt
handful of ice cubes

Kiwi, nectarine and grape
smoothie
2 kiwi fruit
1 nectarine (or peach)
150g grapes
handful of ice cubes

Green smoothie (70 calories per serving)
Wash the spinach, roughly chop the celery and core and chop the apple. Put them into a blender with the rest of the ingredients. Blitz until smooth, then serve and drink right away.

Banana, strawberry and blueberry smoothie (103 calories per serving)
Peel the banana and hull the strawberries, then put them into a blender with the rest of the ingredients. Blitz until smooth, then serve and drink right away.

Kiwi, nectarine and grape smoothie (104 calories per serving)
Peel the kiwi fruit and remove the stone from the nectarine (or peach), then put them into a blender with the rest of the ingredients. Blitz until smooth, then serve and drink right away.

HAM, CORN AND CHILLI MUFFINS

120 calories per muffin

We've always loved the Texas cornbread we featured in Mums Know Best *and these muffins were inspired by that recipe. They make an awesome treat for brunch – or any time of day. We've cut right back on the fat in these and they still work really well, but do watch out for them sticking to the muffin cases. Best thing to do is to mist each case with a spray of oil.*

Makes 12
Prep: 15 minutes
Cooking time: 20 minutes

oil, for spraying
1 tsp lemon juice
250ml semi-skimmed milk
250g self-raising flour
2 tsp baking powder
1 tsp smoked paprika
½ tsp chilli powder
½ tsp dried oregano
50g Parma ham (or other well-
  flavoured ham), finely chopped
100g canned sweetcorn
2 medium eggs, beaten
25g reduced-fat Cheddar cheese,
  finely grated

Preheat the oven to 200°C/Fan 180°C/Gas 6. Line a muffin tin with paper cases and lightly spray each case with oil.

Add the lemon juice to the milk and leave it to stand for 5 minutes. It will thicken slightly and become similar to buttermilk.

Sift the flour, baking powder, smoked paprika and chilli powder into a large bowl. Add the dried oregano, chopped ham and sweetcorn, then mix everything together well.

Add the beaten eggs to the buttermilk and stir. Make a well in the centre of the flour mixture and pour in the wet ingredients. Stir just enough to combine, keeping the mixing to a minimum.

Spoon a heaped tablespoon of the mixture into each muffin case, then sprinkle some grated cheese over the top. Bake in the oven for 15–20 minutes until cooked. Remove the muffins from the oven and leave to cool – if you can resist them for that long!

SMOKED HADDOCK OMELETTE

428 calories per portion (if serving 2); 285 calories per portion (if serving 3)

The idea for this recipe came from a dish known as omelette Arnold Bennett, after the famous novelist. It was created for him by the Savoy Hotel in London and became a much-loved classic. Our version is much less calorific than the original but is still very good to eat and surprisingly rich.

Serves 2–3
Prep: 20 minutes
Cooking time: 25 minutes

200g smoked haddock fillet
   (preferably undyed)
250ml semi-skimmed milk
1 tbsp cornflour
1 tbsp low-fat crème fraiche
1 tbsp finely chopped chives
oil, for spraying
5 eggs, beaten
25g reduced-fat Cheddar cheese,
   grated
freshly ground black pepper

Put the haddock in a wide saucepan and pour in the milk to cover. Bring to the boil, cover, then turn off the heat and leave to stand for 10 minutes. Strain the milk into a jug, then when the fish is cool enough to handle, break it up into chunks and set it aside. Discard the skin and any stray bones.

Mix the cornflour with a little cold water until you have a smooth paste. Measure 150ml of the cooking milk into a small saucepan and add the crème fraiche. Pour in the cornflour mixture and stir over a gentle heat until you have a thick sauce. Season with pepper, then stir in the haddock and the chives.

Heat a large frying pan and lightly spray it with oil. Pour in the beaten eggs, making sure the whole of the base of the frying pan is evenly covered. When the egg mixture is almost set, pile the haddock mixture over one half of the omelette and sprinkle the cheese on top. Carefully flip the uncovered half of the omelette over the filling and leave to cook for a couple of minutes until the cheese has melted.

Cut the omelette in half or divide into thirds and serve immediately.

FAMILY FAVOURITES

Great family meals are at the heart of our cooking –
recipes that are good for those of us who need to shed
a pound or two but also keep the whole family happy.
We know that many people serve up the recipes from
our Hairy Dieters' books and the rest of the family enjoy
them so much they don't even realise that they are low
in calories! Honestly, since we've been writing the diet
books, these healthy dishes are what we cook for our
own families at home. In this chapter are some more
of our favourites for you to try, such as home-made fish
fingers, turkey chilli and some lip-smacking variations
on meatballs. Give 'em a go.

HOME-MADE BAKED BEANS

veggie: 103 calories per portion; bacon: 131 calories per portion

Everyone loves baked beans and our home-made version is extra tasty while cutting down on the sugar. This is best made with dried beans that you've soaked overnight, but you can whip it up with a couple of cans if need be. We like haricot beans, but you can use anything that takes your fancy. Check the packet for cooking times, though, if you do use different beans.

Serves 8 as a side dish
Prep: 15 minutes, plus soaking time
Cooking time: 1 hour 45 minutes

200g dried haricot or other
    beans (or 2 x 400g cans
    of cooked beans)
2 bay leaves
1 slice of onion
2 cloves
1 onion, very finely diced
1 carrot, peeled and very
    finely diced
1 celery stick, trimmed and very
    finely diced
1 tbsp vegetable oil
150ml vegetable stock
400g can of tomatoes
1 tbsp soy sauce
½ tsp sweet smoked paprika
pinch of ground cloves
flaked sea salt
freshly ground black pepper

Smoky bacon beans
½–1 tsp black treacle
100g smoked back bacon, fat
    trimmed and meat finely diced

If you're using dried beans, soak them overnight in plenty of cold water. Drain the beans, then put them in a large saucepan, add water to cover generously and bring to the boil. Keep skimming off any foam that forms until it turns white. Add the bay leaves, onion slice and cloves and continue to boil for 10 minutes, then turn the heat down and simmer for 45–60 minutes. The beans should be cooked through but not too soft, so check them regularly after 45 minutes. Drain, discarding the cooking liquid, bay, onion and cloves.

Meanwhile, prepare the vegetables. They should be chopped as finely as possible – almost to a purée – so you could use a food processor. Heat the oil in a saucepan, add the vegetables and cook them slowly for 10 minutes. Towards the end of this time, turn up the heat slightly so the vegetables start to caramelise – this adds sweetness to the sauce. Pour in the stock and simmer for 5 minutes, then add the tomatoes, soy sauce, paprika and cloves. Season and leave to simmer for about half an hour until the sauce is well reduced.

Using a stick blender or ordinary blender, purée the sauce until smooth. Tip it back into the pan, then add the beans (freshly cooked or canned). Simmer for 15 minutes to allow the flavours to blend.

Smoky bacon beans
Prepare the beans and veg as above, adding the treacle at the same time as the tomatoes and soy sauce. Start with half a teaspoon, simmer the sauce for a few minutes, then taste and add more treacle if you think it needs it. Fry the bacon in a non-stick frying pan until crisp and brown, then add it to the puréed sauce. Drain off any fat from the pan, then deglaze the pan with a little water and add this to the sauce too. Add the beans and simmer for 15 minutes as above.

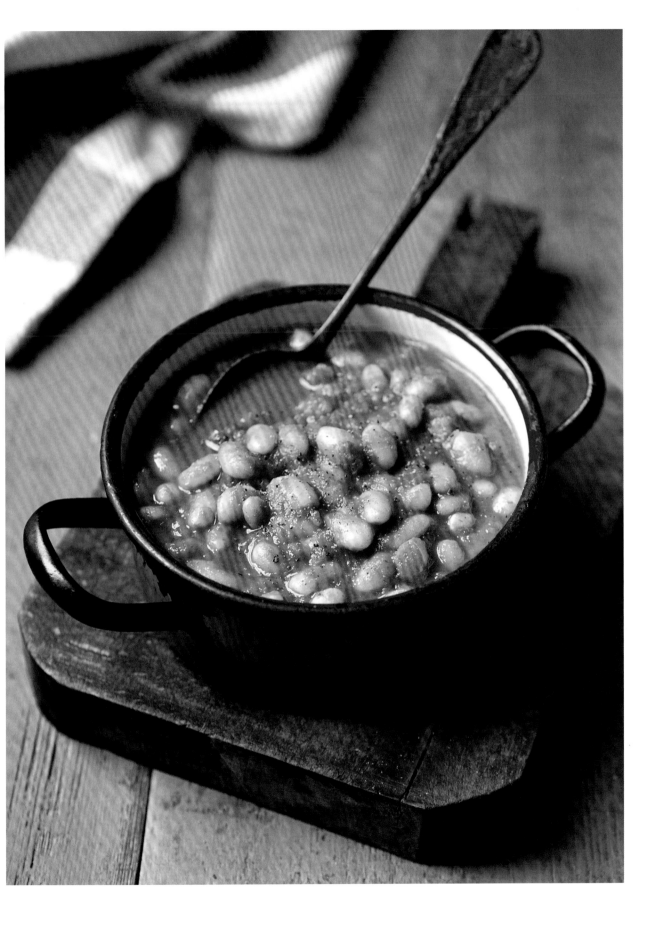

BUBBLE AND SQUEAK

107 calories per portion; 195 calories per portion with poached egg

There's nothing like a good bubble. In our recipe we've upped the carrot and swede and cut down on the potato so it's a bit lighter than usual but still tastes mega. Swede can go a bit mushy when boiled so we like to steam the veg, but if you don't have a steamer, just be sure to drain it all well. You could dry-fry the eggs if you prefer.

Serves 4
Prep: 15 minutes
Cooking time: 15–20 minutes

200g swede, peeled and diced
200g carrots, peeled and diced
200g potatoes, peeled and diced
200g cabbage, shredded
1 tsp olive oil
1 rasher of bacon, fat trimmed
   and meat finely diced
½ onion, finely chopped
4 eggs (optional)
1 tsp white wine vinegar (optional)
flaked sea salt
freshly ground black pepper

Layer the root vegetables in a steamer – swede on the bottom, carrots next, potatoes on top. Steam them over boiling water for 10 minutes or until all the vegetables are tender. If you don't have a steamer, boil the vegetables until tender, then drain them really well. Season the veg and then mash. You don't want the mixture to be too smooth, so don't be too vigorous about it.

Put the cabbage in a saucepan with a couple of centimetres of just-boiled water and simmer it for a few minutes until tender. Drain thoroughly. Add the olive oil to a large non-stick frying pan and fry the diced bacon until brown. Add the onion and cook until it is translucent and taking on a little colour. Tip the bacon and onion into the mash, along with the cabbage, and stir.

Heat the grill to its highest setting. Pile all the mixture into the frying pan and cook over a medium heat for several minutes until you see that it is browning around the edges. Put the pan under the grill until the top has crisped up a bit and is a good deep brown.

If you want to top the mixture with eggs, half fill a medium non-stick saucepan with water, add a teaspoon of vinegar and bring it to the boil. And now for our special tip: place the eggs, still in their shells, into the boiling water for exactly 20 seconds – this helps the whites stay together. Remove them with a slotted spoon and turn the heat down so the water is simmering gently.

Crack the eggs into the water and cook for 3 minutes. The water should be gently bubbling and the eggs will rise to the surface when they are nearly ready. Remove them with a slotted spoon, drain briefly and place an egg on top of each helping of bubble and squeak.

PASTA PUTTANESCA

250 calories per portion

This punchy pasta dish is a great store cupboard stand-by. It's so tasty you really don't need Parmesan as well. Up to you, but giving the cheese a miss does save on calories.

Serves 4
Prep: 8 minutes
Cooking time: 15–20 minutes

1 tsp olive oil
8 anchovy fillets
2 garlic cloves, finely chopped
1 red chilli, deseeded and finely
　　chopped (or 1 tsp chilli flakes)
400g can of tomatoes or 4 large
　　fresh tomatoes, peeled and
　　chopped
100g pitted black olives, sliced
2 tbsp capers, rinsed
pinch of caster sugar (optional)
200g spaghetti
2 tbsp chopped parsley or basil
flaked sea salt
freshly ground black pepper

To make the sauce, heat the olive oil in a frying pan and add the anchovy fillets. Break them up with a wooden spoon, then add the garlic and chilli and fry for a couple of minutes before adding the tomatoes. Season with pepper – not salt at this stage. Simmer for about 15 minutes, then add the olives and capers and continue to simmer for a little longer – you want the sauce to be well reduced. Taste for seasoning and add salt if necessary. You might also want to add a pinch of caster sugar if the tomatoes are on the acidic side.

Meanwhile, bring a large saucepan of water to the boil and add salt. Drop in the spaghetti and cook until it is al dente. This should take 10–12 minutes, but check the packet instructions.

Drain the spaghetti and add it to the pan with the sauce. Mix thoroughly so the sauce coats all the spaghetti, then divide between bowls, making sure everyone gets plenty of sauce. Sprinkle with chopped parsley or basil and serve with a nice big green salad on the side.

FREEZE!

The sauce freezes well. To defrost, put it in a saucepan with a splash of water, then cover and heat gently until warmed through. Serve with freshly cooked pasta.

BAKED FISH WITH RED PEPPERS AND TOMATOES

200 calories per portion

This is a breeze to put together with some good cod, haddock or other fish and it's so good to eat. It's a great family supper but also good to serve when friends come over – let everyone open their own parcels at the table and enjoy the wafts of delicious saffrony, basily aromas. And it's so low cal that you can enjoy a few steamed new potatoes and green beans alongside.

Serves 4
Prep: 15 minutes
Cooking time: 20–25 minutes

1 tsp olive oil
1 red onion, sliced into thin wedges
2 red peppers, deseeded and sliced
  lengthways into strips
2 garlic cloves, finely chopped
1 mild red chilli, deseeded and
  finely chopped
100ml white wine
pinch of saffron threads
200g canned tomatoes (or fresh)
2 tbsp finely chopped parsley
2 tbsp finely chopped fresh basil
1 tsp grated lemon zest
oil, for spraying
4 thick fish fillets, about 150g each
4 thin slices of lemon
flaked sea salt
freshly ground black pepper

Preheat the oven to 200°C/Fan 180°C/Gas 6.

Heat the oil in a large non-stick frying pan. Add the onion and red peppers and fry them over a medium heat until they start to soften – you want them to stay fairly firm. Add the garlic and chilli and cook for another 2 minutes, stirring regularly.

Pour the white wine into the pan and crumble in the pinch of saffron. Simmer until most of the wine has evaporated, then add the tomatoes. Cook over a low heat for another 5 minutes, then stir in the parsley, basil and lemon zest.

Cut 4 large pieces of baking parchment or foil – they need to be big enough to make a parcel for each fish fillet. Spray each piece lightly with oil and place a fish fillet in the middle. Season with salt and pepper, then put a thin slice of lemon on top and add a quarter of the red pepper and tomato mixture to each parcel. Bring 2 opposite edges of the paper or foil together and fold them together. Fold over the remaining 2 edges to seal the parcel neatly. Wrap the remaining parcels in the same way.

Place the parcels on a baking tray and put them in the oven. Bake for 12–15 minutes, then open one slightly and check that the fish is cooked through. Take the parcels to the table so that everyone can open their own and enjoy the sensational scents.

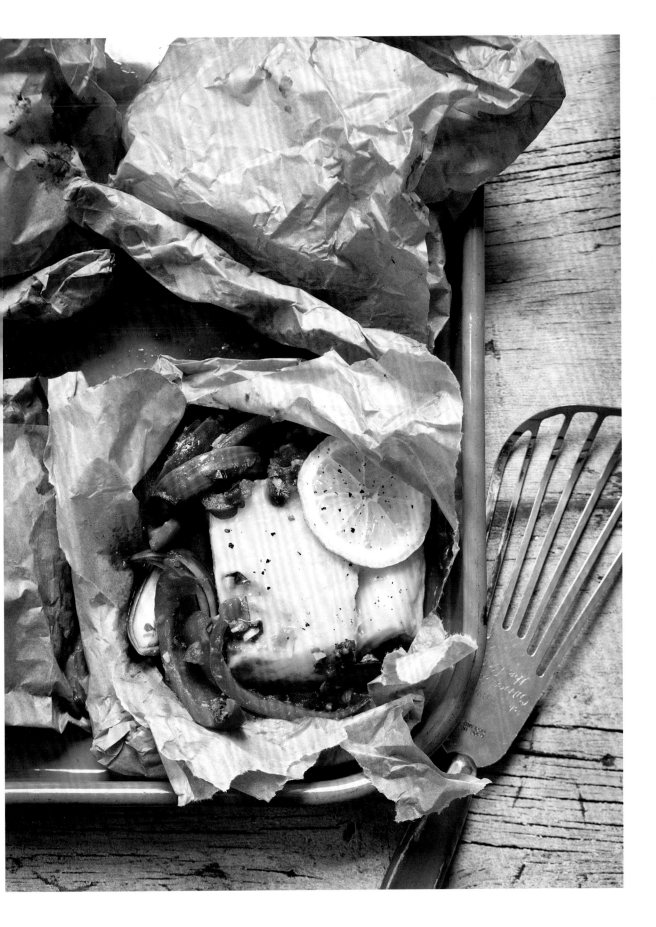

HOME-MADE FISH FINGERS

300 calories per portion

It's not only kids who love fish fingers! We do too and our home-made version beats the packet ones hands – or fingers – down. Spraying them with a bit of extra oil before cooking helps to give them a lovely golden colour and doesn't add many calories. We like these made with salmon but you can also use white fish, such as cod or haddock, which is lower in calories. And how about treating yourself to a fish finger wrap!

Serves 4
Prep: 10 minutes
Cooking time: 8–10 minutes

600g thick skinless salmon fillet
1 tbsp plain flour
1 tsp dried herbs (oregano or a mixture)
1 tsp finely grated lemon zest
4 tbsp low-fat natural yoghurt
50g fine breadcrumbs (such as Japanese panko)
oil, for spraying
flaked sea salt
freshly ground black pepper

Preheat the oven to 220°C/Fan 200°C/Gas 7. Line a baking tray with baking parchment.

Cut the fish fillets into 8 thick fingers. It's best to cut across the fillet if you can but don't worry if your fingers aren't perfectly even. Make sure they are completely dry by blotting with kitchen paper if necessary.

Mix the flour, herbs and grated lemon zest in a bowl and season with salt and pepper, then spread the mixture out on a plate. Spoon the yoghurt into a shallow bowl and spread the breadcrumbs on another plate.

Dip the fish fingers into the flour, shaking off any excess on to the plate. Then dip the flour-coated fish fingers into the yoghurt, again shaking off any excess, and lastly into the breadcrumbs, making sure they get a thorough coating.

Put the fish fingers on the lined baking tray and give them a light spray of oil – this isn't essential, but it will just help the colour along a little. Bake in the oven for 8–10 minutes, until they're starting to turn golden all over. Serve with some green veg or a salad and perhaps a dollop of ketchup – but don't forget to add 20 calories per spoonful!

PRAWN AND TURKEY BALLS

312 calories per portion

You could use chicken for these cheeky little morsels, but turkey mince is readily available in supermarkets and slightly leaner than chicken. You'll see that the ingredients in the broth mirror those in the balls so everything in our Asian fantasia goes together beautifully. Clever eh? Remember that there are no calories in flavour so up the quantities of herbs and spices if you like.

Serves 4
Prep: 15 minutes
Cooking time: 15–20 minutes

250g raw prawns (shelled weight), roughly chopped
250g turkey mince
15g fresh root ginger, grated
2 garlic cloves, finely chopped
juice and grated zest of ½ a lime
a few coriander stems, chopped
1 tbsp fish sauce
50g breadcrumbs
flaked sea salt
freshly ground black pepper

Broth
400g can of reduced-fat coconut milk
200ml chicken stock
2 garlic cloves, finely chopped
15g fresh root ginger, chopped
1 shallot or half a small onion, finely sliced
2 tbsp chopped coriander stems
juice and grated zest of 1 lime
1 tbsp fish sauce
1 tsp sugar
1 red pepper, deseeded and cut into strips
100g baby corn
250g sprouting broccoli or pak choi
red chillies, sliced, to serve
coriander leaves, to serve

To make the prawn and turkey balls, put all the ingredients in a food processor and whizz them together to make a very smooth textured mixture. Leave the mixture to chill for half an hour and then, using damp hands, roll it into balls of about 35g each. You should end up with 16 balls. Chill the balls in the fridge until you are ready to cook them.

To make the broth, pour the coconut milk and chicken stock into a large wok or saucepan. Bring to the boil, then turn the heat down to a simmer and add the garlic, ginger, shallot, coriander stems, lime juice and zest, fish sauce and sugar. Allow the flavours to blend for a couple of minutes, then add the vegetables. Remove the balls from the fridge and add them to the broth, then simmer for about 10 minutes.

Check the broth for seasoning, then sprinkle over a couple of sliced chillies and some torn coriander leaves.

FREEZE!

You can freeze this as is, broth and all, but without the broccoli which will go soggy. Leave the broccoli out and add it to the broth when reheating.

TRANSYLVANIAN MEATBALLS WITH GARLIC SAUCE

432 calories per portion (if serving 4); 288 calories per portion (if serving 6)

There's a double whammy of garlic in this indulgent recipe so it really keeps the vampires at bay! The meatballs cook beautifully in the oven and there's no need to brown them, as the paprika gives a lovely ochre colour. Great with a salad such as the fattoush on page 128.

Makes about 20 meatballs
Prep: 15 minutes
Cooking time: 20 minutes

1 tsp vegetable oil
1 onion, finely chopped
1 green pepper, deseeded
  and finely chopped
4 garlic cloves, finely chopped
600g lean beef mince
1 tbsp sweet paprika
100g breadcrumbs, Japanese panko
  are ideal
50g low-fat natural yoghurt
flaked sea salt
freshly ground black pepper

Garlic sauce
1 head of garlic, cloves separated
  but unpeeled
100g low-fat natural yoghurt
a pinch of caster sugar
1 tsp white wine vinegar

FREEZE!

The meatballs can be frozen raw or cooked, but don't freeze the sauce.

Preheat the oven to 220°C/Fan 200°C/Gas 7. Line a baking tray with baking parchment.

Heat the oil in a frying pan. Add the onion and green pepper and cook, stirring regularly, until the onion is soft and translucent. Add the garlic cloves and cook for another 2 minutes, then remove the pan from the heat and allow the veg to cool.

Put the beef in a large bowl and break it up. Season generously with salt and pepper and sprinkle over the paprika and breadcrumbs. Add the cooled onion, pepper and garlic, along with the yoghurt and mix the whole lot together. The easiest way to do this thoroughly is with your (very clean) hands.

Form the mixture into balls of about 40g each – the size of a golfball. Space them evenly on the baking tray and bake them in the oven for 12–15 minutes, until well browned.

Garlic sauce

To make the sauce, bring a small saucepan of water to the boil and add all the unpeeled garlic cloves. Simmer until the cloves are very tender – this should take about 15 minutes. Drain the garlic cloves and rinse them under cool running water until cool enough to handle. Squeeze the flesh out of the skins and then mash them on a chopping board with a fork.

Put the yoghurt in a bowl and add the mashed garlic, sugar and white wine vinegar. Season with salt and pepper and leave to stand for a few minutes before serving with the meatballs.

SMASHED-UP CHICKEN

316 calories per portion

You might recognise the title of this recipe from one of our earlier books. It makes a little chicken go a long way and was a great favourite but quite high-cal so we've tweaked and fiddled and got it down to a reasonable level for our new svelte selves. We've cut down on the fat content, reduced the amount of pasta a little, upped the veg and it still tastes the business.

Serves 4
Prep: 15 minutes
Cooking time: 25 minutes

4 skinless, boneless chicken thighs
1 tsp olive oil
200g button mushrooms, wiped and quartered
1 leek, trimmed and sliced into rounds
100ml white wine
125ml chicken stock
2 garlic cloves, crushed
1 tbsp fresh tarragon, finely chopped
1 tbsp lemon juice
freshly grated zest of 1 lemon
2 tbsp capers (rinsed and drained)
2 tbsp low-fat crème fraiche
handful of flatleaf parsley, chopped, to serve
flaked sea salt
freshly ground black pepper

Pasta
200g pasta (penne, fusilli – whatever you like)
1 tsp olive oil
1 tsp chilli flakes
1 garlic clove, crushed

Put a chicken thigh between 2 pieces of cling film and beat it with a rolling pin until thin. We really do want you to smash the chicken to bits, so don't be shy. Peel off the top layer of cling film and pull the chicken off in thin strips or ribbons. Repeat with the remaining thighs and season the chicken with salt and pepper.

Heat the oil in a non-stick frying pan. Cook the strips of chicken over a high heat until they are turning golden brown and just cooked through – this shouldn't take more than a couple of minutes, as the chicken strips are so thin. Take the chicken out of the pan and add the mushrooms. After a couple of minutes of cooking, they should start giving out some liquid. At this point, add the leek and sauté both together until the leek has started to soften.

Add the wine and stock to the pan and bring to the boil, stirring constantly to make sure nothing sticks to the bottom. Continue to cook to reduce the liquid and finish cooking the leek, then add the garlic, tarragon, lemon juice and zest. Cook for another 2 minutes, then add the capers.

Remove the pan from the heat and stir in the crème fraiche. Put the chicken back in the pan and warm it through again on a gentle heat. Check the seasoning.

Meanwhile, cook the pasta in plenty of salted, boiling water according to the packet instructions. Heat the olive oil in a separate pan, add the chilli flakes and garlic, then cook for just a minute. When the pasta is done, drain it well, then toss it in the chilli/garlic oil. Mix the chicken with the pasta and serve with plenty of chopped parsley sprinkled on top.

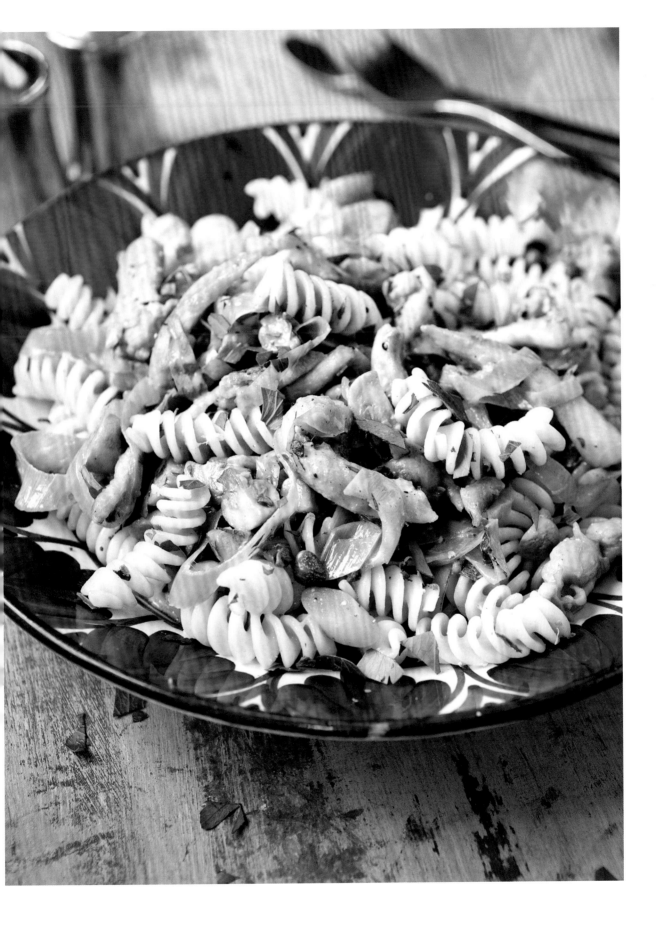

TURKEY CHILLI WITH CAULIFLOWER 'RICE'

300 calories per portion (with cauliflower); 240 calories (without cauliflower)

You can add a tiny bit of chocolate to this chilli which gives it a lovely rich mouth feel, but don't be tempted to eat the rest of the bar! Instead of serving the chilli with regular rice, try our cauliflower version, which tastes great and is very low calorie. Chipotle paste is available in supermarkets and delivers a real kick to the dish.

Serves 4
Prep: 15 minutes
Cooking time: 45 minutes

1 tsp vegetable oil
1 red onion, finely chopped
1 large red pepper, deseeded
  and diced
2 celery sticks, trimmed and diced
4 garlic cloves, finely chopped
500g turkey mince
1 tsp dried oregano
2 bay leaves
1 tbsp ground cumin
½ tsp ground allspice
1 tbsp chipotle paste
400g can of chopped tomatoes
400g can of beans (kidney, pinto,
  black-eyed peas), drained and
  rinsed
15g dark chocolate
flaked sea salt
freshly ground black pepper

To serve
fresh coriander leaves
lime wedges, for squeezing
low-fat crème fraiche

Cauliflower rice
1 cauliflower, broken up into florets
1 tsp cumin seeds
a small bunch of fresh coriander,
  chopped
flaked sea salt
freshly ground black pepper

Heat the oil in a large saucepan, then add the onion, pepper and celery. Cook over a low heat for 5 minutes, until the veg are starting to soften, then add the garlic and the turkey mince. Turn up the heat slightly and cook until the turkey has browned all over. Keep stirring and use the spoon to break up any clumps of turkey mince.

Add the oregano, bay leaves, cumin, allspice and chipotle paste. Give everything a good stir so it all gets coated with the paste, then pour in the chopped tomatoes and 250ml water. Add the drained beans and season with salt and pepper.

Bring to the boil, then cover the pan and simmer the chilli over a low heat for half an hour, until the sauce has thickened. Keep an eye on it and add a drop more water towards the end if you think it is in danger of catching. Five minutes from the end of the cooking time, add the chocolate. To serve, divide between 4 plates, sprinkle with coriander leaves and add a wedge of lime and a dessertspoon of crème fraiche to each serving.

Cauliflower rice
Break the cauliflower up into florets. Put these in a food processor and blitz until the cauliflower has the texture of large breadcrumbs.

Heat a non-stick frying pan and dry-fry the cumin seeds for a few moments until they start to give off a spicy aroma. Coat the bottom of the pan with water – about 100ml should do it. Evenly spread the cauliflower crumbs over the frying pan and season. Cook over a medium heat for about 5 minutes, stirring fairly regularly until the water has evaporated and the cauliflower is looking quite dry. Stir in the coriander and remove the pan from the heat. Fork the cauliflower over and it will 'fluff up' nicely.

CHICKEN WITH CITRUS RUB AND BRAISED LENTILS

chicken: 166 calories per portion; chicken and lentils: 400 calories per portion

Slicing the chicken through the middle into thin pieces means it cooks really quickly and stays tender. The citrus rub adds bags of flavour and is so easy to do. This recipe makes plenty of rub mixture but it keeps well for another time. It's best to get unwaxed fruit if you can, but otherwise give the lemons and oranges a good scrub in hot water to melt off the wax. The chicken is great with the braised lentils but also good with the Greek roast veg on page 136.

Serves 4
Prep: 25 minutes
Cooking time: 1 hour 45 minutes

4 skinless, boneless chicken breasts
1 tsp olive oil

Rub
finely grated zest of 2 oranges
finely grated zest of 1 lemon
2 long sprigs of rosemary
10g black peppercorns
25g coarse salt

Braised lentils
1 tsp olive oil
1 onion, finely chopped
2 celery sticks, trimmed and diced
2 carrots, peeled and diced
100g mushrooms, wiped clean
   and finely chopped
2 garlic cloves, finely chopped
a few sprigs of thyme
1 tsp sage
150g puy lentils (or green or
   brown lentils)
75ml white wine
600ml chicken stock or water
1 tbsp tomato purée
2 tbsp finely chopped parsley
flaked sea salt
freshly ground black pepper

First make the rub. Preheat the oven to its lowest setting and line a tray with baking parchment. Spread the zest and rosemary over the baking tray. Put the tray in the oven for half an hour, then remove and break up any clumps of zest. Put the tray back in the oven for another hour, adding the peppercorns for the last 10 minutes. Remove from the oven and allow the mixture to cool. Tip it all into a spice grinder with the salt and whizz until you have a fairly fine powder. Decant the powder into a jar – it will keep indefinitely.

Now for the chicken. Using a sharp knife, cut into the middle of the breast and continue slicing until you have cut the breast into 2 thin pieces. Put a slice between 2 pieces of cling film and flatten with a meat hammer or rolling pin until it is about 5mm thick. Repeat with the remaining breasts.

Dust the rub all over the chicken. You won't need much – perhaps half a teaspoon per piece. Heat the oil in a large frying pan. Add a few pieces of chicken and cook on one side for 2 minutes or until they are a deep golden brown, then flip them over and cook on the other side for 2–3 minutes. Check whether the chicken is done – if it isn't, cook for another minute or so. The exact time will depend on the thickness of your chicken but make sure that no pinkness remains. Keep the chicken warm while you cook the rest.

Braised lentils
Heat the oil in a large saucepan. Add the onion, celery, carrots and mushrooms to the pan and cook, stirring regularly, over a medium heat until the veg are starting to brown round the edges. Add the garlic and cook for another 2 minutes, then add the thyme and sage.

Rinse the puy lentils well and add them to the saucepan. Pour over the wine and stock and season with salt and pepper. Bring the mixture to the boil and cover the pan with a lid. Simmer for 15 minutes, then add the tomato purée.

Simmer uncovered for another 15 minutes until the lentils are tender, stirring regularly to check that there is enough liquid in the pan. If you think the lentils are in danger of sticking, add a little more water or stock. Sprinkle with parsley before serving.

FRIDAY NIGHT SUPPERS

It's Friday night, you're looking forward to the weekend and you feel like a treat, but you don't want to undo all your good work. Fear not – there's no need to be tempted by the local kebab shop when you can try some of our mouth-watering versions of dishes like samosas, beef curry and stir-fries. And you won't believe our special fusion tandoori chicken, coated with a mix of curry paste, dill and capers. Sounds bonkers but it's a taste sensation.

PRAWN STIR-FRY WITH COURGETTE 'NOODLES'

180 calories per portion

We were dead chuffed with the lasagne we made using pieces of leek instead of pasta in our first Hairy Dieters' book, so we thought we'd try making noodles with strips of courgette! They're fab and ridiculously low calorie. Be warned – when you prepare the courgettes they will look like a huge heap but they do wilt down a lot so don't worry. There's a lovely little Thai lilt to this dish and we're sure you'll enjoy it.

Serves 4
Prep: 20 minutes
Cooking time: 8–10 minutes

400g large peeled raw tiger prawns,
    deveined if necessary
1 small bunch of coriander leaves,
    stems and leaves separated
2 large courgettes
1 tbsp vegetable oil
1 onion, sliced into thin wedges
1 red pepper, sliced into strips
1 carrot, cut into matchsticks
100g green beans, cut in half
100g baby corn, sliced in half
    lengthways
1 tbsp soy sauce
225g can of bamboo shoots,
    drained
100g bean sprouts

Marinade
2 garlic cloves, crushed
1 small red chilli, deseeded and
    finely chopped
1 lemon grass stalk, finely sliced
freshly squeezed juice and finely
    grated zest of 1 lime
10g chunk of fresh root ginger,
    peeled and grated
2 tbsp fish sauce
1 tsp caster sugar

Put the prawns in a bowl. Put all the marinade ingredients and the coriander stems in a food processor or blender and blitz until well combined – the mixture doesn't have to be very smooth. Pour this over the prawns and stir well so they are all coated. Set aside while you prepare the vegetables.

Top and tail the courgettes. Using a vegetable peeler, cut them into long strips, making them as thin as you can. Cut these strips in half lengthways until you have a large pile of noodle-like ribbons of courgette, each about 1cm wide.

Heat the oil in a wok or large frying pan until it's at smoking point and add the onion, red pepper and carrot. Cook over a very high heat for 2 minutes, stirring constantly, then add the green beans and baby corn. Continue to cook over a very high heat for another couple of minutes, then add the soy sauce. Finally, add the bamboo shoots, bean sprouts and courgettes. Turn everything over for a minute until the courgette noodles start to wilt. Be careful here – if you cook them for too long they will start to collapse and give out too much water. You want them to stay nice and firm.

Divide the vegetables between your serving plates, then immediately throw the prawns, with their marinade, into the wok. Stir over a high heat until the prawns are just cooked through and starting to char slightly. Add the prawns to the vegetables and serve immediately with the coriander leaves sprinkled over.

SAMOSAS

71 calories per meat samosa; 65 calories per veggie samosa

Over the years we've come up with a number of samosa recipes – they're a guilty pleasure we don't want to give up. These work a treat and we've found that you can bake them in the oven instead of deep-frying, so saving lots of calories.

Makes 18
Prep: 30–45 minutes
Cooking time: 30–45 minutes

6 sheets of filo pastry
oil, for spraying

Meat filling
1 tbsp vegetable oil
175g lean chicken or turkey mince
1 onion, finely chopped
50g butternut squash, peeled and
    finely diced
2 garlic cloves, finely chopped
5g chunk of fresh root ginger,
    peeled and finely chopped
1 tsp garam masala
1 tsp nigella seeds
½ tsp turmeric
50g peas (fresh or frozen)
squeeze of lemon juice
2 tbsp finely chopped coriander
    leaves
flaked sea salt
freshly ground black pepper

To make the meat filling, heat the oil in a non-stick frying pan and add the mince and onion. Cook for 5 minutes until the meat is cooked through and the onion has softened. Add the squash, garlic and ginger and cook for another 2 minutes. Add the garam masala, nigella seeds and turmeric, then pour in 100ml of water. Add the peas and season with salt and pepper. Simmer over a gentle heat until the squash is tender and most of the liquid has evaporated. Add a squeeze of lemon juice, then stir in the chopped coriander. Leave the filling to cool at least to room temperature before you start assembling the samosas.

To make the vegetable filling, heat the oil in a non-stick frying pan. Add the onion and potato and cook, stirring regularly, for 5 minutes until soft. Proceed with the remaining ingredients exactly as for the meat filling and leave to cool.

To make the shells for the samosas, lay out a sheet of filo. Cut out rounds measuring about 16cm in diameter. You should be able to get 3 rounds from each sheet. You can make a template out of cardboard for this, or find a plate or bowl that is about the right size.

Fold a round in half to make a semi-circle and place it with the straight side at the bottom. Take the outer right corner and fold the pastry over so it overlaps half of the rest of the semicircle of pastry. Take the outer left corner and fold it over the rest of the pastry to make a cone shape. Wet the outside edges and press to make sure they are securely stuck to the rest of the pastry.

Open up the cone and make sure there are 3 layers of pastry on each side. Add about a dessertspoon of filling – do this a teaspoon at a time so you can get more filling into the bottom corner of the cone. Make sure you leave a border around the top of at least half a centimetre. Fold one side of the border down on top of the filling, then dampen each of the 3 layers of remaining border and fold this over to close the samosa. Make sure there are no loose edges and pinch each of the 3 corners. Repeat to use all the filo and stuffing.

When you are almost ready to bake the samosas, preheat the oven to 220°C/Fan 200°C/Gas 7. Place the samosas on a baking tray and spray them lightly with oil. Bake in the preheated oven for 15–20 minutes until crisp and golden brown in patches.

Vegetable filling
1 tbsp vegetable oil
1 onion, finely chopped
200g potato, finely diced
2 garlic cloves, finely chopped
5g chunk of fresh root ginger, peeled and finely chopped
1 tsp garam masala
1 tsp nigella seeds
½ tsp turmeric
50g peas (fresh or frozen)
squeeze of lemon juice
2 tbsp finely chopped coriander leaves
flaked sea salt
freshly ground black pepper

FREEZE!

Samosas are probably best frozen once assembled but uncooked. The bonus is that unlike deep-fried samosas, these seem to stay beautifully crisp and light even when they've cooled down. While you're at it you could make double the quantity.

LAMB DHANSAK

336 calories per portion

This is a proper curry and we've trimmed the calories while keeping it punchy and delicious. Although we love curry pastes, we've discovered that they're higher in calories than powder.

Serves 6
Prep: 20 minutes
Cooking time: 2 hours 15 minutes

1 tbsp vegetable oil
2 large onions, thinly sliced
750g lean lamb leg meat, diced
20g chunk of fresh root ginger, peeled and grated
4 garlic cloves, finely chopped
3 green chillies, deseeded and finely chopped
2 tbsp medium curry powder
1 tbsp ground cumin
1 tbsp ground coriander
1 tsp turmeric
2 bay leaves
150g red lentils
½ butternut squash, cut into large chunks
juice of 1 lime
handful of chopped coriander leaves, to garnish
flaked sea salt
freshly ground black pepper

Heat the oil in a large casserole dish or heavy-based saucepan. Add the onions and cook over a low heat until they have softened but not browned. This should take about 15 minutes. Turn up the heat slightly and add the lamb, ginger, garlic and chillies. Sprinkle all the spices over the meat and season with salt and pepper. Stir for a couple of minutes until the lamb is well coated with spices.

Add the bay leaves and the red lentils, then pour in 700ml water. Slowly bring to the boil, turn the heat down and leave to simmer for an hour. Add the butternut squash and cook for another half an hour, then remove the lid and leave the curry to simmer, uncovered, for another 15 minutes.

Check the seasoning, add the lime juice and sprinkle with chopped coriander before serving. Lovely served with some cauliflower rice (see page 50).

FREEZE!

This freezes well. The flavours of the ginger and garlic will intensify on freezing, but in a good way. Just be careful when defrosting and reheating not to stir too much, as cooked, frozen lamb has a tendency to shred. To avoid soggy butternut squash, prepare the dish up to the point that the butternut squash is added, then freeze and add the squash when reheating.

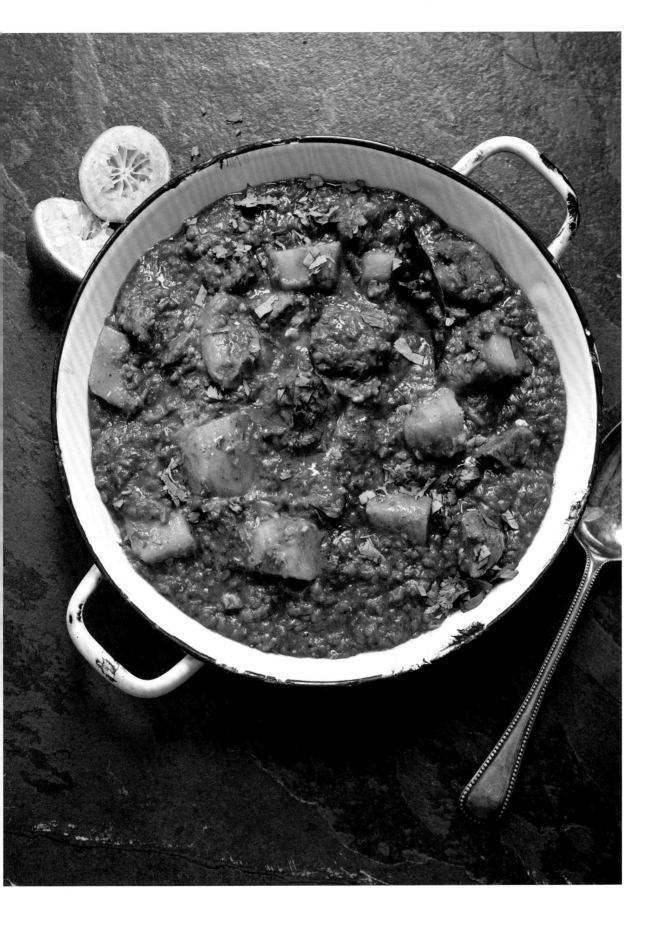

VEGETABLE CURRY

91 calories per portion

There's more fibre in this veggie treat than a brillo pad and it's much tastier of course! Vegetable curries, especially those with aubergine, often contain lots of oil. We've kept the oil as low as possible in this by cooking the aubergine on a fairly high heat so it seals quickly and doesn't soak up too much. The mushrooms also give out some liquid, which helps keep things nice and juicy. Serve with rice for a veggie main meal or as an accompaniment to a meat dish.

Serves 4
Prep: 15 minutes
Cooking time: 30–35 minutes

1 tbsp vegetable oil
1 tsp cumin seeds
1 onion, thickly sliced
1 aubergine, diced
200g mushrooms, wiped
  and halved
1 courgette, diced
2 garlic cloves, finely chopped
10g chunk of fresh root ginger,
  peeled and grated
1 tbsp medium curry powder
100g green beans, halved
400g can of tomatoes
large handful of fresh coriander
  leaves
flaked sea salt
freshly ground black pepper

To serve
4 tbsp fat-free natural yoghurt
1 tsp dried mint (optional)

Heat the oil in a large frying pan and add the cumin seeds, onion, aubergine, mushrooms and courgette. Cook over a medium heat, stirring regularly, until the vegetables have started to soften around the edges and have taken on a bit of colour.

Add the garlic and ginger, then sprinkle over the curry powder and season with salt and pepper. Add the green beans and pour in 200ml of water. Simmer for 2 minutes, then add the tomatoes. Simmer for about 20 minutes, until the vegetables are tender and the curry has thickened.

Just before serving, stir in a large handful of fresh coriander. Serve with yoghurt – stir some dried mint into it if you like.

PIZZAS WITH 3 TOPPINGS

420 calories per meat feast pizza; 322 calories per Parma ham, courgette and mushroom pizza; 405 calories per spinach and egg pizza

The dough recipe will make 4 very thin pizzas of about 20cm in diameter. Don't worry if they're not perfectly round – they look more rustic and taste just as good. Each topping recipe makes enough for four pizzas and the mozzarella is divided between them. Top tip: if you've made our turkey chilli on page 50 and you've got some left over, it makes a brilliant pizza topping!

Serves 4
Prep: 15 minutes, plus 1 hour rising time
Cooking time: 26–40 minutes

Pizza dough
250g strong white flour
5g dried yeast
½ tsp salt
150ml tepid water

Tomato sauce
400g can of tomatoes
2 garlic cloves
1 tsp dried oregano
large handful of basil, shredded
flaked sea salt
freshly ground black pepper

1 ball of half-fat mozzarella, very
   thinly sliced

Meat feast
1 tsp olive oil
1 onion, finely chopped
200g lean beef mince
1 tsp ground cumin
1 tsp ground coriander
2 tbsp sliced jalapeño chillies
1 red pepper, deseeded and sliced
   thinly into rounds

To make the pizza dough, mix the flour, yeast and salt, then gradually add the water until you have a dough. Either turn the dough out on to a floured work surface and knead until smooth and elastic (about 5 minutes) or knead with the dough hook in a food mixer. Put the dough in a bowl and cover with a damp tea towel. Leave until it has doubled in size – this will probably take about an hour. Knock it back and cut it into 4 pieces – best to do this by weight.

To make the sauce, put the tomatoes, garlic and oregano in a saucepan and season with salt and pepper. Simmer until the tomatoes have reduced to a thick paste – 20–30 minutes. Add the basil, then blitz with a blender until smooth.

Preheat your oven to its highest setting and heat a couple of upturned baking trays. Roll each ball of dough out into a round of about 20cm in diameter. Put a couple of spoonfuls of sauce on each base and spread it over evenly. Add 3–4 slices of mozzarella to each pizza, then finish with your chosen topping (see below). Slide the pizzas on to the hot baking trays – you should be able to get 2 on each. Bake for about 6 minutes.

Meat feast topping
Heat the oil in a frying pan and add the onion. Fry over a medium heat until the onion has softened and is starting to go brown, as this will add sweetness. Add the beef, then sprinkle over the spices. Season with salt and pepper and fry until the beef is just cooked through. Divide this mixture between the pizzas and top with the jalepeños and red pepper.

Parma ham, courgette and mushroom topping

Sprinkle the grated courgette and the sliced mushrooms over the tomato sauce on the pizzas. Tear up each slice of Parma ham and arrange it on top and sprinkle over the herbs.

Spinach and egg topping

Wash the spinach thoroughly, then without draining it too thoroughly, put it in a saucepan and cook until it has wilted down completely. Wait until it is cool enough to handle, then squeeze out as much of the moisture as you can. Season with salt, a grating of nutmeg and the lemon zest. Divide the spinach between the 4 pizzas. The best way to arrange it is in a circular 'wall', large enough to contain the egg. Break an egg on to each pizza and sprinkle over the Parmesan cheese.

Parma ham with courgettes
and mushrooms
½ courgette, grated
8 mushrooms, wiped and thinly
    sliced
4 slices of Parma ham
a few sprigs of thyme
basil leaves, roughly torn

Spinach and egg
200g fresh spinach
a grating of nutmeg
1 tsp finely grated lemon zest
4 eggs
10g Parmesan cheese, finely grated

SWEDISH MEATBALLS

473 calories per portion (if serving 4); 315 calories per portion (if serving 6)

These will bring back memories of the meatballs served at a certain Scandinavian megastore but they are really easy to make at home. Stick some Abba on and enjoy our Swedish supper – you'll be living the dream!

Serves 4–6 (makes about 24 meatballs)
Prep: 20 minutes
Cooking time: 40 minutes

1 tbsp olive oil
1 onion, finely chopped
1 garlic clove, finely chopped
300g lean beef mince
300g lean pork mince
1 tbsp anchovy paste
100g breadcrumbs
50ml milk
½ tsp allspice
¼ tsp nutmeg
1 tsp flaked sea salt
freshly ground black pepper
a few sprigs of dill, to serve

Gravy
100ml white wine
500ml well-flavoured beef stock
2 tbsp single cream
1 tbsp lingonberry jam, melted and
  sieved if you want to get rid of
  the fruit (or redcurrant
  or cranberry jelly)
up to 1 tbsp arrowroot
flaked sea salt
freshly ground black pepper

Preheat the oven to 200°C/Fan 180°C/Gas 6. To make the meatballs, heat the oil in a frying pan and cook the onion until it's soft and translucent. Add the garlic and cook for another minute. Remove the pan from the heat and allow the onion and garlic to cool.

Put all the meatball ingredients, including the onion and garlic, into a large bowl and mix thoroughly with your hands. Shape the mixture into balls between the size of a walnut and a golf ball – they should be about 40g in weight. Put the balls on a baking tray and bake for 12–15 minutes until cooked through.

To make the gravy, put the wine in a saucepan and boil fiercely until it has reduced by about half – this is to cook most of the alcohol taste out of it. Add the stock and simmer for 5 minutes, then stir in the single cream and the jam. Season with salt and pepper. Mix the arrowroot with a little water and add a teaspoon of the mixture at a time to the gravy, stirring thoroughly and simmering briefly between each addition until it has started to thicken.

Put the meatballs in the gravy and simmer for another 5 minutes to allow all the flavours to combine – this is important for the taste of the gravy so don't be tempted to skip this stage. Serve with a sprinkling of dill.

FREEZE!

The cooked meatballs freeze well. Open freeze them on a tray, then pop them into freezer bags or a plastic box once they're solid. The gravy is best made fresh. Gently reheat the defrosted meatballs in the gravy before serving.

LEMON CHICKEN

186 calories per portion

Great served with plain rice and some Chinese greens or steamed pak choi. The trick with the egg white is called velveting and gives an authentic Chinese texture to the chicken.

Serves 4
Prep: 10 minutes, plus 20 minutes chilling
Cooking time: 10–12 minutes

4 fairly small chicken breasts
   (about 100–150g each) sliced
   into strips
1 egg white
2 tsp cornflour
1 tbsp vegetable oil
2 spring onions, sliced, to serve

Sauce
100ml chicken stock
juice of 2 lemons
1 tsp caster sugar
1 tbsp light soy sauce
1 tbsp rice wine (mirin)
3 garlic cloves
½ tsp chilli flakes
½ tsp cornflour
a few drops of sesame oil
flaked sea salt
freshly ground black pepper

Put the chicken strips in a bowl. Whisk together the egg white and cornflour, making as smooth a paste as you can. Pour this over the chicken and mix thoroughly so the chicken is completely coated. Chill for 20 minutes in the fridge.

Heat the oil in a wok until it starts to smoke then add all the chicken. Toss the chicken around the wok until it is golden brown and completely cooked through, with no sign of pinkness. This shouldn't take longer than a couple of minutes. Remove the chicken from wok and set aside.

To make the sauce, put the wok back on the hob but over a lower heat. Add the chicken stock, lemon juice, sugar, soy sauce, rice wine, garlic cloves and chilli flakes and season well with salt and pepper. Bring to the boil, then turn the heat down and simmer for a minute.

Mix the cornflour with a small amount of water until you have a smooth, thin paste. Pour this into the sauce and simmer until the sauce has thickened slightly. Put the chicken back in the wok and simmer until it has warmed through again. Finally, add a few drops of sesame oil.

Let the whole thing sit for a few minutes to allow the flavours to develop – this is important for the final taste of the sauce. Sprinkle with the sliced spring onions before serving.

CARIBBEAN CHICKEN CURRY

290 calories per portion

This is a proper carnival of a dish and has everything you need in one scrumptious pot full of Caribbean flavours. You can buy Caribbean curry powder in most supermarkets.

Serves 4
Prep: 20 minutes
Cooking time: 1 hour 30 minutes

8 bone-in chicken thighs,
   skinned and trimmed of fat
1½ limes
1 tbsp vegetable oil
300ml chicken stock or water
1 large sprig of thyme
2 bay leaves
200g piece of pumpkin, peeled
   and cut into large chunks
1 large potato, peeled and cut
   into large chunks
100g pineapple, diced
1 tsp rum (optional)
2 spring onions, finely sliced
2 tbsp chopped flatleaf parsley
flaked sea salt
freshly ground black pepper

Curry paste
1 onion, roughly chopped
4 garlic cloves, peeled and cut
   in half
15g chunk of fresh root ginger,
   peeled and roughly chopped
2 scotch bonnet chillies (or to
   taste), deseeded and finely
   chopped
2 tbsp medium curry powder,
   preferably Caribbean
½ tsp ground allspice

Put the chicken thighs in a bowl and add the juice of 1 lime and about 100ml of water. Rub the lime juice over the chicken and leave for a few minutes while you make the paste.

For the paste, put the onion, garlic, ginger, scotch bonnets, curry powder and ground allspice in a food processor or blender and add a tablespoon of water. Blitz until fairly smooth.

Heat the vegetable oil in a large casserole dish over a medium heat. Add the paste and cook, stirring constantly, for a couple of minutes. Now add the chicken and season with salt and pepper. Stir so the chicken is coated with the paste, then pour in 300ml of chicken stock or water and add the thyme and bay leaves.

Bring the mixture to the boil, then turn down the heat to a gentle simmer and cover. Cook for about 45 minutes, then add the pumpkin, potato and pineapple. Cook for another 30 minutes, covered, then take off the lid. Add the juice of the remaining half a lime and, if you like, a teaspoon of rum, then cook, uncovered, for another 10 minutes to allow the sauce to reduce a little. Sprinkle the spring onions and parsley over the top of the curry and serve.

FUSION TANDOORI CHICKEN

214 calories per portion (2 drumsticks); 321 calories per portion (3 drumsticks)

We originally created this bit of fusion confusion for salmon but tried it with chicken and it was even better. You'll think that mixing tandoori spice, dill and capers sounds like a crazy idea but trust us, it really works! And it's so low cal you can serve some rice and salad alongside.

Serves 4–6
Prep: 10 minutes, plus at least 1 hour marinating time
Cooking time: 20–25 minutes

12 chicken drumsticks, skinned
100g low-fat natural yoghurt
2 tbsp chopped dill
2 tbsp capers
100g tandoori paste
1 tsp chilli powder (optional)
lemon wedges, to serve
flaked sea salt

Cut slashes in the flesh of the drumsticks, then put them in a bowl and season with salt. Put the yoghurt, dill and capers in a blender or food processor and blitz until the capers and dill are finely chopped. Mix this with the tandoori paste, and the chilli powder if you want some extra heat, then pour the lot over the chicken.

Make sure the paste covers the chicken – the best way to do this is to massage it into the cuts with your hands. Cover and leave to marinate for at least an hour, but preferably overnight.

When you're ready to cook the chicken, preheat the oven to its highest setting. Put a wire rack over a roasting tin. Take the drumsticks out of the marinade and place them on the rack. Bake for 20–25 minutes, turning occasionally, until the drumsticks are well cooked and starting to blacken in places.

Serve with lemon wedges to squeeze over the chicken.

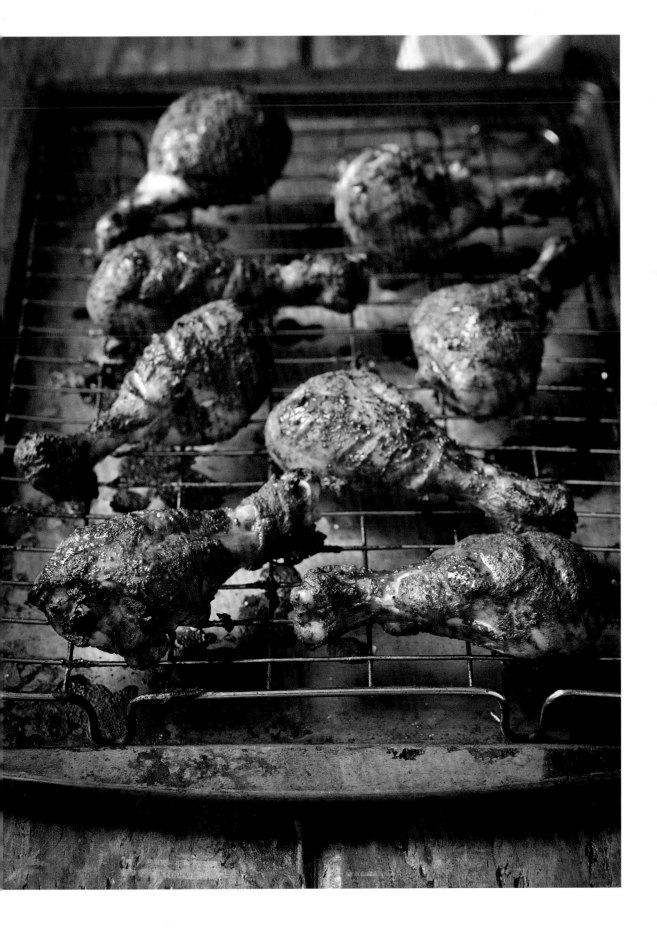

CHICKEN STIR-FRY

196 calories per portion

We learned so much when filming in Asia last year and we've tried to put our discoveries to good use in our latest healthy recipes. There are some traditional Chinese flavours in this stir-fry and as it's packed with veg you'll have generous servings. Once you've prepared everything for this dish it's cooked and on the table in the blink of an eye. Just be sure to cook the bean sprouts very briefly so they don't wilt and give off too much water in the wok.

Serves 4
Prep: 15 minutes, plus
20 minutes chilling
Cooking time: 6–8 minutes

2 chicken breasts, cut into
   thin strips
1 egg white
2 tsp cornflour
1 tbsp vegetable oil
300g tenderstem broccoli,
   halved lengthways
1 large red pepper, deseeded
   and cut into strips
100g mushrooms, wiped clean
   and cut in half
2 garlic cloves, finely sliced
15g chunk of fresh root ginger,
   peeled and finely chopped
2 red chillies, finely diced
   (deseeded if you like)
4 spring onions, sliced into rounds
225g can of water chestnuts,
   drained
150g bean sprouts
2 tbsp light soy sauce
2 tbsp rice wine (mirin)
4 tbsp chicken stock or water
1 tsp curry powder
½ tsp sesame oil
flaked sea salt
freshly ground black pepper

Put the chicken strips in a bowl. Whisk together the egg white and cornflour, making the paste as smooth as possible. Pour this over the chicken and mix thoroughly so the chicken is completely coated. Chill for 20 minutes in the fridge.

Heat the oil in a wok. Fry the chicken strips for one minute, until well browned and almost cooked through. Remove them from the wok, leaving behind as much oil as possible. Add the broccoli, red pepper and mushrooms and cook them over a high heat for 2 minutes, then add the garlic, ginger, chillies and sliced spring onions. Stir-fry for a further minute, then add the water chestnuts and bean sprouts.

Put the chicken back in the wok. Mix the soy sauce with the rice wine, chicken stock or water and curry powder in a bowl. Pour this mixture over the contents of the wok, season with salt and black pepper, then cook, stirring constantly for another 2 minutes.

Check that the chicken is cooked through, with no pinkness remaining, and cook for slightly longer if necessary. Just before serving, drizzle a little sesame oil on top.

BEEF AND COCONUT CURRY

559 calories per portion (if serving 4); 447 calories (if serving 5)

This is based on an amazing dish we ate in a roadside café in Kerala back in 2005. We featured it in our curry book but this new version is lower in calories and just as good to eat. We've given details for a fab spice mix, which tastes brilliant, but if you're short of time and don't have all the spices, just use the garam masala with the fennel seeds and it will still be good. Great with roast cauli which adds just 25 calories per portion.

Serves 4–5
Prep: 20 minutes, plus at least 1 hour marinating
Cooking time: 2 hours 20 minutes

800g lean stewing steak, cut into chunks
2 onions, finely sliced
15g chunk of fresh root ginger, peeled and grated
4 garlic cloves, sliced
1 green chilli, deseeded and finely chopped
1 tbsp red wine vinegar
200ml coconut milk
1 tbsp vegetable oil
a handful of coriander leaves, chopped
sliced green chillies, to serve (optional)

Spice mix
4 cloves
2 tsp fennel seeds
1 tbsp coriander seeds
1 tsp chilli flakes
1 tsp ground turmeric
½ tsp ground cinnamon
2 tsp flaked sea salt
or
2 tsp fennel seeds
2 tsp garam masala
2 tsp flaked sea salt

First make the spice mix. Grind the cloves, fennel seeds, coriander seeds and chilli flakes in a spice grinder or pestle and mortar, then mix with the turmeric, cinnamon and salt. Alternatively, grind the fennel seeds and mix with the garam masala and salt. Put the beef in a large bowl and sprinkle over the spice mix. Add half the onions with the ginger, garlic, chilli and vinegar and mix well. Leave to marinate for at least an hour.

Put a heavy saucepan or heatproof casserole dish on top of the stove over a medium heat. Add the beef, along with its marinade, and pour in the coconut milk. Slowly bring to the boil, then turn the heat down, cover and cook on a very low heat for about an hour and a half, until the beef is tender. You will find that a lot of liquid comes out of the beef but don't worry – this is meant to happen.

When the beef is tender, remove the lid, turn up the heat to medium, then simmer the curry quite fiercely until all the liquid has evaporated. This will take up to half an hour and be sure to keep stirring every few minutes to make sure the meat doesn't catch on the bottom.

Once the liquid has reduced, heat the oil in a large frying pan. Add the remaining sliced onion and cook for a few minutes over a medium heat until the onion is golden brown. Add the beef mixture and continue to fry for 5–6 minutes until the meat is well browned and looks rich and gorgeous. Sprinkle with chopped coriander and chillies, if using, then serve with roasted spiced cauliflower.

Roast spiced cauliflower

Preheat the oven to 200°C/Fan 180°C/Gas 6. Bring a large pan of water to the boil and add the cauliflower florets. Cook for 2 minutes, then drain and leave to dry out in the colander.

Give the seeds a light pounding with a pestle and mortar or bash them with a rolling pin. Put the cauliflower in a roasting dish and toss with the vegetable oil. Sprinkle over the spices and the lime zest and juice, then season. Roast in the oven for about 15 minutes, until the cauliflower has started to brown round the edges. It should still be slightly firm.

Roast spiced cauliflower
½ head of cauliflower, broken into
   small florets
1 tsp vegetable oil
1 tsp nigella seeds (optional)
1 tsp cumin seeds
1 tsp coriander seeds
1 tsp mustard seeds (optional)
grated zest and juice of 1 lime
flaked sea salt
freshly ground black pepper

WEEKEND FEASTS

Weekends can be tricky when you're trying to lose a bit of weight. We know what it's like – you want to have a few friends over or to treat the family but you don't want to stray too far from your diet. With our weekend feasts you can keep everyone happy. We've included a few low-cal dishes you can enjoy as starters for a special dinner, such as piri piri prawns and our super scallop dish. Then you might like to serve up steak and kidney pie, coq au vin or our fab turkey crown roast, all carefully calorie counted. Delight your chums and keep yourself on track.

PIRI PIRI PRAWNS

130 calories per portion

These succulent prawns with a hit of chilli make a great starter for a special meal and can be cooked on a barbecue or indoors on a griddle pan. You'll need some bamboo or metal skewers. If you're a real chilli fiend you could add a couple of chopped bird's eye chillies to the marinade.

Serves 4
Prep: 15 minutes, plus marinating
Cooking time: 4–6 minutes

600g large peeled tiger prawns, deveined if necessary
lemon wedges, to serve

Marinade
4 plump red chillies, deseeded and roughly chopped
4 garlic cloves, peeled
20g bunch of flatleaf parsley (with stalks)
freshly squeezed juice of 2 lemons (about 65ml)
2 tbsp white wine vinegar
1 tsp smoked paprika
1 tsp oregano
1 tsp caster sugar
2 tsp flaked sea salt

To make the marinade, put all the ingredients in a food processor and blitz until everything is chopped quite finely and well combined.

Rinse the prawns in cold water and drain well, then put them in a bowl and cover with the marinade. Stir thoroughly to make sure the prawns are completely coated. Cover the bowl with cling film and leave the prawns to marinate in the fridge for at least a couple of hours. You can leave them overnight if you like.

If you're using bamboo skewers, soak them in water for half an hour before using to prevent them from burning. Thread the prawns on to the skewers. When your barbecue or griddle is hot enough, cook the prawns for 2–3 minutes on each side, until they have turned pink and opaque and have charred slightly. Be careful not to overcook them, though. Serve with lemon wedges – try popping them on the grill for a few minutes. They look great and produce lots of juice.

Top tip from us – these prawns are best eaten with your fingers!

SCALLOPS WITH CORAL SAUCE
AND CAULIFLOWER PURÉE

142 calories per portion

We know that some people chuck away the coral from scallops. Seems a bit of a waste to us, as they're very tasty. Try our trick of whipping the corals up into a nice colourful topping for your scallops in this dish, which makes a cracking dinner party starter.

Serves 4 as a starter
Prep: 10 minutes
Cooking time: 15–20 minutes

12 scallops, with corals
1 tsp vegetable oil
1 shallot, finely chopped
4 tbsp fat-free natural yoghurt
pinch of cayenne
squeeze of lemon juice
oil, for spraying
pea shoots, for serving (optional)
flaked sea salt
freshly ground black pepper

Cauliflower purée
½ head of cauliflower, broken
   into florets
1 tbsp fat-free natural yoghurt
flaked sea salt

To make the cauliflower purée, bring a saucepan of water to the boil and add salt. Add the cauliflower and simmer for about 5 minutes, until it's soft. Strain and leave the cauliflower to drain for a few minutes. Blitz the cauli in a blender and add the yoghurt to make a purée. Tip this back into the pan and cover to keep it warm while you make the coral sauce and cook the scallops.

Separate the scallops from the corals and pull off the membrane. Heat the oil in a small frying pan and cook the shallot over a medium heat until it's soft and starting to caramelise. Turn the heat up towards the end of the cooking time to allow the shallot to brown more, but be careful not to let it burn.

Remove the shallot from the frying pan and add all the corals. Fry for a minute on each side, then remove them from the pan. Add a splash of water to the frying pan and stir, scraping up any brown bits of coral or shallot.

Put the shallot, corals, any liquid from the frying pan and the yoghurt into a blender. Season with salt and pepper and a pinch of cayenne, then blitz until smooth. Add a tiny squeeze of lemon juice and push the sauce through a sieve into a small saucepan to make it super-smooth. Heat gently while you sear the scallops.

Spritz a large frying pan with oil and put it over a medium heat. Add the scallops and sear for a couple of minutes on each side, pressing them down with a spatula so they take on a good colour.

Serve the scallops on small mounds of the cauliflower purée and top with spoonfuls of coral sauce. Sprinkle with pea shoots if you like.

LETTUCE OR CHICORY CUPS WITH
SMOKED DUCK AND ORANGE

37 calories per cup

Serve these little duck delights as a light starter or as canapés with drinks – we might be watching our weight but we're still dead posh. Use chicory or little gem lettuce leaves or some of each.

Makes 12
Prep: 10–15 minutes

1–2 heads of chicory or little gem
   lettuces
1 orange
175g smoked duck, skin removed
1 mild red chilli, finely diced
small bunch of fresh coriander,
   leaves only

Dressing
juice from segmenting the orange
1 tbsp olive oil
1 tsp sherry vinegar
1 tsp mustard
1 tsp honey
flaked sea salt
freshly ground black pepper

Cut the base off the chicory or little gems and separate out the best-shaped leaves. The leaves need to look fairly compact and cup-like, so they can hold the rest of the ingredients and should be of a size that can be eaten in one mouthful, so trim as necessary. You can use any leftover leaves in a salad.

Slice the top and bottom off the orange and place it on a chopping board, resting it on one of the flat ends. Using a sharp knife, cut off the peel and pith, working your way around the fruit. Next, cut between the membranes to release the segments. Do this over a bowl to catch any juice, then squeeze the remaining membrane and the discarded pieces of skin to extract as much juice as possible.

Dice the smoked duck and mix it with the red chilli.

For the dressing, add the reserved orange juice to the other ingredients and whisk everything together well.

To assemble, put a generous 2 teaspoons of the duck and chilli mixture on each leaf. Top with a piece of orange, drizzle over some of the dressing and finally sprinkle over some chopped coriander. Serve at once.

COQ AU VIN

400 calories per portion

This is our 'love in a transit' recipe rewritten to cut the calories but with no compromise on comfort or flavour. Lovely with some celeriac purée (see page 90) to soak up the juices.

Serves 4
Prep: 30 minutes, plus marinating
Cooking time: about 1 hour
30 minutes

———

300ml red wine
½ onion, finely chopped
1 carrot, peeled and finely diced
1 celery stick, trimmed and
    finely diced
4 garlic cloves, chopped
a few sprigs of thyme
2 bay leaves
1 clove
1 tbsp plain flour
4 bone-in, skinless chicken thighs
4 skinless chicken drumsticks
1 tbsp olive oil
4 rashers of back bacon, diced
400g button onions or shallots,
    peeled
250g button mushrooms,
    wiped clean
500ml chicken stock
1 tbsp redcurrant jelly
finely chopped parsley, to serve
flaked sea salt
freshly ground black pepper

Pour the wine into a saucepan and add the onion, carrot, celery, garlic, herbs and clove. Bring to the boil and boil fiercely for about 5 minutes to reduce the liquid a little and concentrate the flavours. Remove the pan from the heat and leave to cool. Put the chicken in a dish and once the liquid is cool, pour it over the chicken and leave to marinate for at least a few hours, or overnight if possible.

Spread the flour on a plate and season it with salt and pepper. Remove the chicken pieces from the red wine marinade and pat them dry with kitchen paper. Set the marinade aside for later. Dust the chicken pieces in flour and set aside.

Heat the oil in a large casserole dish. Add the bacon and brown it quickly, then transfer it to a plate with a slotted spoon and add the button onions, or shallots, and the mushrooms to the pan. Fry over a high heat for a minute, then turn the heat down and cook for about 10 minutes, stirring regularly, until the onions are nicely golden. Remove the onions and mushrooms from the dish, leaving behind as much oil as you can for browning the chicken. Add the chicken pieces and brown them on each side.

Put the bacon, onions and mushrooms back in the casserole dish, then strain the marinade through a sieve and pour this into the dish. Add the stock and redcurrant jelly. Bring everything to the boil, then turn the heat down to the lowest of simmers and cook, uncovered, for about an hour. After an hour everything should be tender and the sauce should be reduced.

If you want a slightly thicker sauce, remove the chicken, bacon and vegetables with a slotted spoon and put them on a warm serving dish. Bring the remaining liquid back to the boil and cook for a few minutes until it has reduced further, then pour it over the chicken. Check the seasoning and sprinkle with parsley before serving.

TUSCAN DEVIL'S CHICKEN

252 calories per portion (if serving 4); 168 per portion (if serving 6)

This is a great simple barbecue recipe or it can be cooked indoors if the weather is bad. It's also great cold for a picnic or lunch box.

Serves 4–6
Prep: 10 minutes, plus
marinating
Cooking time: 10–15 minutes

12 boneless, skinless chicken
  thighs, trimmed of fat

Marinade
2 tbsp black peppercorns
juice of 2 lemons
1 tsp dried oregano
1 tsp olive oil

First, you need to flatten the chicken thighs. Open out a few so they are lying flat and place them between 2 large sheets of cling film. Now give them a good bashing with the smoother end of a meat mallet – or the bottom of a saucepan or a rolling pin will do fine. Repeat with the remaining thighs.

Put the chicken thighs in a bag with all the marinade ingredients. Close the top of the bag and massage the marinade well into the thighs, then leave them in the fridge for at least 2 hours or overnight if possible.

When you are ready to cook the chicken, heat your barbecue or a griddle pan on the hob. Brush most of the marinade off the chicken thighs and place them on the hot barbecue rack or griddle. Cook on one side for several minutes. When they are nicely charred on the underside, turn them over (you should be able to remove them quite easily at this point) and grill the other side until the chicken is completely cooked through and no trace of pinkness remains. As the thighs have been flattened, the cooking process shouldn't take longer than 10 minutes.

If you prefer, you can bake the chicken. Preheat the oven to 220°C/ Fan 200°C/Gas 7. Line a large baking tray with baking parchment and space the pieces of chicken out on the tray. Bake for about 15 minutes until the meat is cooked through, basting with any remaining marinade at intervals.

Great served with our tabbouleh (see page 126) or other salads.

CHICKEN CHASSEUR

307 calories per portion

There's a reason why dishes like this are classics – it's because they're so good. Easy to make, this is a really tasty treat and delicious served with some celeriac purée to soak up the flavoursome juices.

Serves 4
Prep: 25 minutes
Cooking time: about 1 hour

8 bone-in, skinless chicken thighs, trimmed of fat
1 tbsp flour
2 tsp olive oil
2 shallots, finely chopped
2 garlic cloves, finely chopped
250g mushrooms, wiped clean and quartered
100ml white wine
1 tbsp tomato purée
300ml chicken stock
200g fresh tomatoes, peeled and chopped (or canned equivalent)
2 tbsp chopped tarragon leaves
flaked sea salt
freshly ground black pepper

Celeriac purée
1 large or 2 small celeriac, peeled and cut into small chunks (you need about 1kg peeled weight)
2 garlic cloves, roughly chopped
1 tbsp low-fat crème fraiche
flaked sea salt

FREEZE!

This can be frozen. Defrost thoroughly and reheat gently so you don't break up the chicken too much.

Before starting to cook, take each chicken thigh and place it bone-side up on your work surface. Cut either side of the bone so you can flatten the thigh out slightly – this helps it cook evenly. Season the chicken thighs with salt and pepper, then dust them with flour.

Heat a teaspoon of the oil in a large frying pan and add the chicken thighs. Cook them for a couple of minutes on each side until golden brown, then remove them from the pan and set aside – you might need to do this in a couple of batches. Turn the heat down and add the remaining teaspoon of olive oil to the pan. Add the shallots, garlic and mushrooms and fry over a very gentle heat for several minutes, stirring regularly, until everything has softened without taking on much colour.

Pour in the white wine and let it bubble, stirring with a wooden spoon to loosen any sticky bits from the bottom of the pan. Stir in the tomato purée, making sure it blends with the wine, then add the stock, tomatoes and tarragon. Put the chicken back in the pan. Simmer, uncovered, for about 40 minutes until the chicken is cooked through and tender, and the sauce has reduced. If it looks as though the pan is becoming too dry, add a splash of water. Serve with celeriac purée and some green veg or salad.

Celeriac purée

Put the celeriac and garlic in a medium-sized saucepan and cover with water. Season with a little salt. Bring up to simmering point, then cover and leave to cook over a low heat for about 15 minutes. Drain the celeriac and garlic in a colander, then tip everything back into the pan and mash well or purée with a stick blender. Stir in the crème fraiche, check the seasoning and serve.

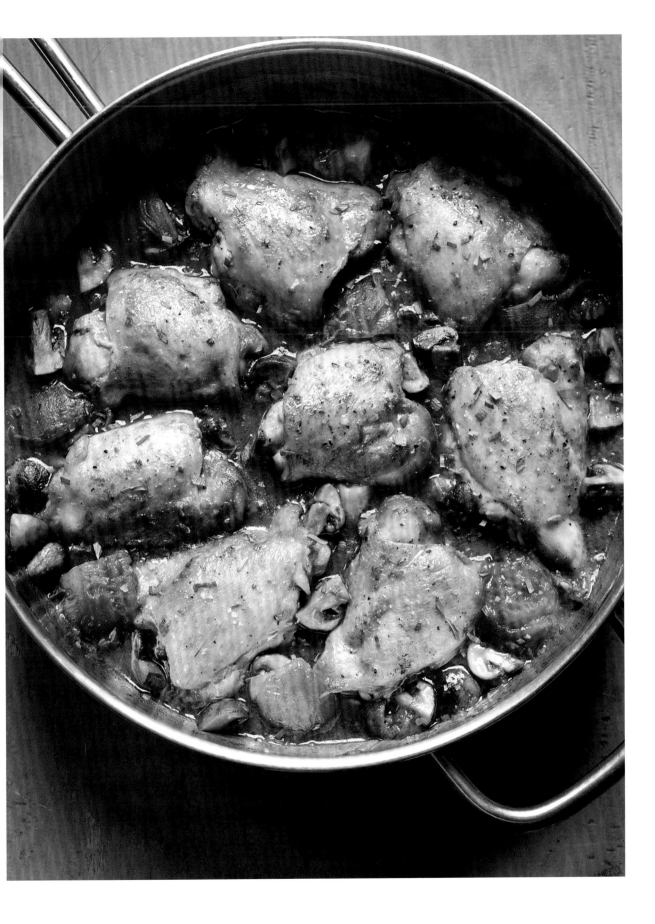

POT-ROAST PORK WITH CIDER AND APPLES

277 calories per portion

Lean pork meat is not high in calories, but don't kid yourself that crackling or pork fat can ever be low cal. It has to be trimmed off. Pork and apple work as well together as Fred and Ginger – or Si and Dave – and the cider in this recipe makes for a beautifully fragrant, yet light gravy. We find that it's best to use eating apples, such as Coxes, for this. Bramleys fall apart too much. The sauce is great as it is, but you can thicken it with a little arrowroot if you prefer.

Serves 6
Prep: 15 minutes
Cooking time: 1 hour
and 15–30 minutes

1 tbsp olive oil
1kg piece of rolled pork shoulder
   or loin, trimmed of fat
2 onions, sliced
6 garlic cloves, unpeeled
1 tsp dried sage or 1 tbsp fresh sage,
   chopped
2 bay leaves
300ml cider
2 eating apples, peeled,
   cored and sliced
flaked sea salt
freshly ground black pepper

Preheat the oven to 200°C/Fan 180°C/Gas 6.

Heat the oil in a large casserole dish. Season the pork with salt and black pepper, place it in the dish and brown it on all sides. Remove the pork and set it aside, turn down the heat and add the onions. Cook them slowly for about 10 minutes until they have softened but don't let them brown. If they start to catch, add a splash of water.

Put the pork back in the casserole dish and add the garlic and herbs. Pour in the cider. Cover the dish with a lid and place it in the preheated oven for 45 minutes. Remove the dish from the oven and add the apples, then put it back for another 15–30 minutes until the pork is cooked through and tender.

Transfer the pork to a warm serving dish and leave it to rest. Strain the cooking liquid, reserving the apples and onions. Remove the garlic, squish the flesh from the skins, then whisk it into the cooking liquid – chuck the skins away. You will have a very thin, creamy-looking gravy.

Serve the pork cut into thick slices, garnished with the onions and apples and a good glug of gravy.

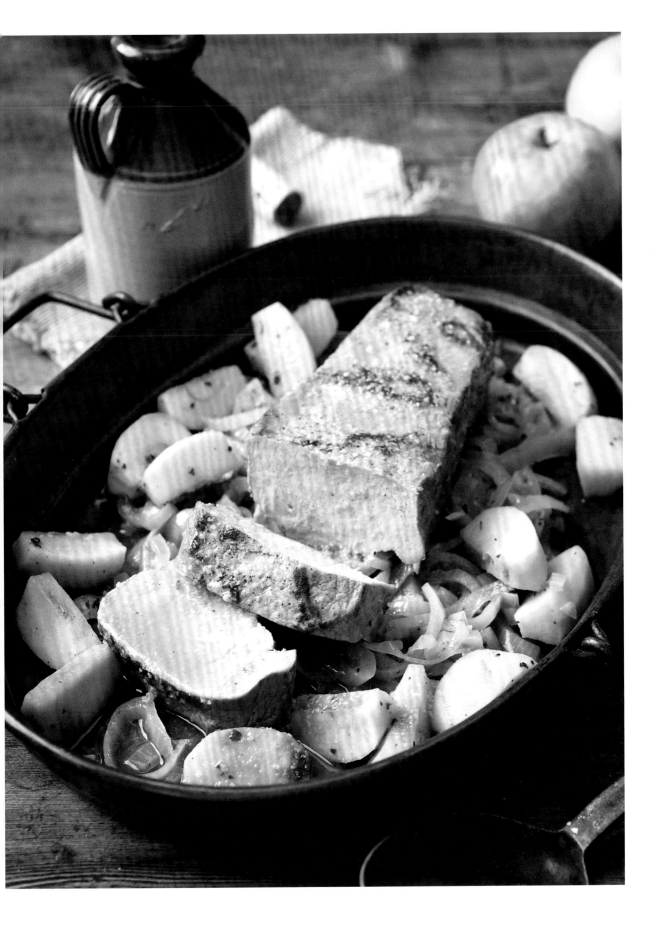

ROAST TURKEY CROWN WITH SWEET POTATO, MUSHROOM AND CHESTNUT STUFFING AND GRAVY

321 calories per portion (100g of turkey and all the trimmings);
373 calories per portion (150g of turkey and all the trimmings)

This is the answer to everyone who has been asking what to do for Christmas dinner or a big celebration when you're trying to watch the calories. Just don't gobble down too much!

Serves 6 (with leftovers)
Prep: 45 minutes
Cooking time: 1 hour 45 minutes

1 turkey crown (2–3kg, depending on how many you want to feed)
1 large onion, sliced widthways into even slices
1 large sprig of tarragon
150ml white wine
1 tsp flour (optional)
flaked sea salt
freshly ground black pepper

Stuffing
½ onion, finely chopped
2 celery sticks, finely chopped
100g mushrooms, wiped clean and finely chopped
150g sweet potato, finely chopped
100g chestnuts, finely chopped (vacuum-packed are fine)
2 rashers of streaky bacon, finely chopped
1 tsp chopped thyme leaves
1 tsp dried oregano

Roast potatoes and parsnips
600g potatoes
300g parsnips
oil, for spraying

First make the stuffing, chopping the vegetables and chestnuts in a food processor if you like. Heat a non-stick frying pan and add the bacon. Cook until some of the fat renders out, then add all the other ingredients, including the herbs and seasoning. Cook over a fairly low heat for about 10 minutes, until everything starts to soften, then turn up the heat and cook for a few more minutes to caramelise the veg a little. Remove the pan from the heat and leave the stuffing to cool. Weigh the stuffing and add this to the weight of the turkey so you can work out the cooking time.

Preheat the oven to its highest setting. Take the turkey out of the fridge half an hour before you want to cook it. Loosen the skin around the neck end (between the fattest part of the breasts). When the stuffing is cool, fill the neck cavity – it should hold all the stuffing. Pull the skin over tightly and secure it with a skewer. Put the onion slices in the middle of a roasting tin and add the tarragon. Lie the turkey crown on top, then pour in the wine and 150ml of water and season with salt and pepper.

Put the turkey in the oven and roast at the high temperature for 30 minutes. Turn the oven down to 180°C/Fan 160°C/Gas 4 and cook for another 12–15 minutes per kilogram. Make sure the turkey is cooked by piercing the thickest part with a skewer. The juices should run clear and the tip of the skewer should be almost too hot to touch. If the juices are still pink, cook for a little longer.

Remove the turkey and onions from the roasting tin, cover with foil and leave to rest for 20 minutes. The meat juices in the tin will be lovely as they are, so you can just put the tin over a low heat, stir well to lift any dark, caramelised bits, then strain into a warm jug.

If you want to thicken the gravy, pour off the juices, put the tin over a low heat and sprinkle over a teaspoon of flour. Stir, making sure you scrape up any of the bits sticking to the tin, then pour the liquid back in, a little at a time, until you have a thick gravy. Carve the turkey and serve with the gravy, stuffing, roast potatoes and parsnips and some green veg.

Roast potatoes and parsnips

Bring a saucepan of water to the boil. Add the potatoes and parsnips and simmer for 5 minutes to parboil. Drain the veg in a colander, then shake them around a bit to roughen up the edges. Tip them into a roasting tin or baking tray, then spritz with oil and season.

Put the potatoes and parsnips into the oven once the turkey has had its first 30 minutes at the high temperature. When you take the turkey out of the oven, whack the temperature up to 200°C/Fan 180°C/Gas 6 so the veg can finish cooking while the turkey rests.

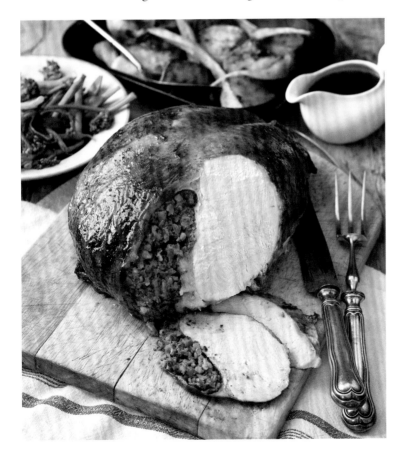

STEAK PIZZAIOLA

317 calories per portion (without cheese);
369 calories per portion (with cheese)

This is so easy to prepare and a real treat to eat. There are lots of different recipes for this dish, some including peppers, mushrooms and so on, but we prefer to keep it simple and enjoy the wonderful flavour combination of tomato sauce and steak. And if you like you can top it all off with a little melted cheese.

Serves 2
Prep: 15 minutes
Cooking time: 25–35 minutes

4 large very ripe tomatoes
1 tbsp olive oil
2 shallots, finely chopped
2 garlic cloves, crushed
1 tbsp fresh oregano or 1 tsp dried oregano
pinch of caster sugar (optional)
1 lean rump steak (about 325g), 2cm thick
salad leaves, to serve
25g hard cheese such as Cheddar or Gruyère, very thinly sliced (optional)
flaked sea salt
freshly ground black pepper

First peel the tomatoes. To do this, score a small cross in the base of each and put them in a small bowl. Cover the tomatoes with freshly boiled hot water, count to 10, then remove them from the water. The skins will slip off easily. Chop the tomatoes and set them aside.

Heat the olive oil in a non-stick frying pan. Add the shallots and fry over a medium heat for several minutes until they're soft and translucent. Add the garlic and cook for 2 minutes more, stirring regularly. Now add the oregano and tomatoes and bring everything to the boil. Simmer the sauce for about 15 minutes until well reduced, then taste for seasoning and add a little sugar if needed.

Trim as much fat off the steak as you can, then season the meat with salt and pepper. Cut the steak in half. Heat a griddle pan for several minutes until it is as hot as you can get it, then add the steaks. Grill them for 2–3 minutes on each side or according to taste. Transfer them to a board and leave to rest for a few minutes.

Once the steaks have rested, strain any meat juices into the tomato sauce. Cook the sauce for another minute to allow the juices to combine. Lay the steaks on warm plates, then spoon over the sauce and serve immediately, garnished with some salad leaves.

If you want to add cheese, heat the grill to its highest setting while you're cooking the steaks, but cook the steaks for a minute less on the second side. When the steaks have rested, put them in an ovenproof dish, cover with tomato sauce, then top with the cheese. Put the dish under the hot grill until the cheese has melted and started to brown.

STEAK AND KIDNEY PIE

400 calories per portion

This is one of our favourite pies, made with our special potato pastry – the next instalment in our quest for a great but low-cal pie crust. If you're not keen on kidneys, you can use mushrooms instead, which will cut the calorie count down a little. You'll need about 200g of button mushrooms. Cut them in half and add them towards the end of the onions' cooking time.

Serves 6
Prep: 40 minutes, plus pastry chilling time
Cooking time: 2 hours 30 minutes

Filling
750g braising steak, trimmed of all fat and cut into 2.5cm cubes
3 lambs' kidneys, cores removed and meat diced
1 tbsp flour
1 tsp mustard powder (optional)
1 tbsp vegetable oil
2 large onions, sliced lengthways
100ml red wine
a few sprigs of thyme
1 bay leaf
500ml beef stock
1 tsp Worcestershire sauce
flaked sea salt
freshly ground black pepper

Pastry
275g floury potatoes, preferably Maris Pipers or King Edwards
40g chilled butter, diced
80g plain flour
1–2 tbsp semi-skimmed milk
1 egg, lightly beaten, to glaze
pinch of salt

First make the mash for the pastry. Peel the potatoes and cut them into chunks of about 3cm. Put them in a large saucepan, cover with cold water and bring to the boil. Cook for 10–15 minutes or until very tender. Drain the potatoes in a colander, tip them back into the saucepan, then mash until smooth – don't add any butter or milk. Leave to cool.

To make the filling, put the cubes of beef and kidneys in a bowl. Mix the flour with the mustard powder, if using, and season with salt and pepper. Sprinkle this on to the meat and turn the meat over lightly with your hands, making sure that it all gets a covering.

Heat the oil in a large casserole dish. Add the onions and cook over a very low heat until they're quite soft and translucent. Remove them from the dish. Turn the heat up and add the meat, stirring very quickly until it's coloured all over. Leave the heat turned up and pour in the red wine. Allow it to bubble up, then stir, making sure you scrape up any brown bits stuck to the base of the pan. Add the thyme sprigs and bay leaf, then pour in the beef stock. Add the Worcestershire sauce and tip the onions back into the pan.

Bring everything to the boil, then cover and turn the heat down as low as you can. Simmer gently for about an hour and a half until the meat is tender. Remove the meat and onions from the casserole dish with a slotted spoon and transfer to an oval pie dish. Turn the heat up and boil the remaining liquid until it is thick and gravy-like, then pour this over the meat and onions. Put a pie funnel in the centre of the pie dish if you have one.

To make the pastry, rub the butter into the flour in a bowl, then add 200g of mash and 1 tablespoon of the milk. Season with a pinch of salt. Work everything together into a dough, handling it as lightly as possible. If it's too dry, add a touch more milk, but only a teaspoon at a time. When you have a smooth dough, roll it into a ball, cover it with cling film and chill for at least half an hour.

Preheat the oven to 200°C/Fan 180°C/Gas 6. Roll the pastry out on a lightly floured work surface, until it is large enough to cover your pie dish. It will be fairly thin, about 3mm, but it will be robust enough that it won't break when you lift it. Wet the rim of the pie dish with water. Carefully lift the pastry using the rolling pin and place it over the pie, pressing the edges firmly around the rim of the dish. Cut a hole for the pie funnel if you're using one. For a good colour, glaze the pie with beaten egg. Bake the pie in the preheated oven for 40–45 minutes until the top is a deep golden brown.

CHILLI STEAK SALAD

322 calories per portion (if serving 2); 161 calories per portion (if serving 4)

Like lots of other people, we loved the Thai beef salad in our last book so we've come up with a variation on the theme. Cutting the steak into strips makes it look like you're getting more, which is always encouraging.

Serves 2 as main course
or 4 as a starter
Prep: 15 minutes
Cooking time: 4–6 minutes

1 sirloin steak, about 400g
100g salad leaves, such as rocket,
    watercress, baby spinach
12 radishes, quartered
½ cucumber, halved and cut into
    very thin rounds
4 spring onions, halved widthways
    then shredded
small bunch of coriander, chopped
flaked sea salt
freshly ground black pepper

Dressing
2 garlic cloves, finely chopped
15g chunk of fresh root ginger,
    peeled and grated
1–2 red chillies, finely chopped
    (deseeded if you like)
2 tbsp fish sauce
freshly squeezed juice of 1 lime
1 tsp caster sugar

First make the dressing. Mix together all the ingredients, stirring until the sugar has dissolved. Taste and season with salt and pepper, then set aside.

Heat a griddle pan until it is as hot as you can get it. Trim the steak of any visible fat and season with salt and pepper. Cook the steak on the griddle for 2–3 minutes on each side or according to taste – although medium rare is probably best for this dish.

Put the steak on a board and leave it to rest for a few minutes. Arrange the salad ingredients on a large platter, or on individual plates if you prefer.

Slice the steak into thin strips, then pour any meat juices into the dressing and stir. Arrange the meat on top of the salad, then pour over the salad dressing. Serve at once.

COMFORT CLASSICS

There are some great old favourites in this chapter –
dishes such as warming tomato soup and Scotch broth
that are always good to come home to. They're like a
lovely cuddle for your tummy. We reckon pasta is the
most comforting, heart-warming food of all so we've
included some of our latest spaghetti suggestions.
And then there are pies. We can't live without our pies
and we now have an amazing new pastry recipe that
you just have to try. It contains mashed potato instead
of some of the flour, which incredibly makes
it lower in calories – surprising and delicious!

TOMATO SOUP

171 calories per portion

Our tomato soup is really rich, creamy and flavoursome – but there's no cream in it, no sugar, just lots of veg. It's a great way of getting the kids to have some of their five a day too. The fennel seeds add an extra tang of flavour but if you don't have any, or don't like them, just leave them out. You could also chill this soup and keep it in the fridge to enjoy as a snack, like gazpacho.

Serves 4
Prep: 15 minutes
Cooking time: 25–35 minutes

1 tbsp olive oil
1 onion, diced
1 celery stick, trimmed and diced
1 large carrot, peeled and diced
1 leek, trimmed and thinly sliced
100g butternut squash, peeled
    and diced
200g celeriac, peeled and diced
1 tsp fennel seeds, ground
    (optional)
2 garlic cloves, finely chopped
50g red lentils
1.2 litres vegetable or chicken stock
400g can of tomatoes
handful of basil leaves, shredded
flaked sea salt
freshly ground black pepper

Heat the olive oil in a large saucepan and add the onion, celery, carrot, leek, squash and celeriac. Sauté over a fairly high heat, stirring regularly, until the vegetables are starting to brown slightly around the edges and give off a sweet aroma.

Add the fennel seeds, if using, and the garlic and sauté for another 2 minutes. Add the red lentils and pour over the stock, then season with salt and pepper. Simmer for 10 minutes.

Add the tomatoes and simmer for another 10–15 minutes until the lentils are completely soft. Add the basil and let it wilt into the soup, then remove the pan from the heat. Purée the soup until smooth, adding more stock or water if it seems too thick for your liking. Taste for seasoning before serving and adjust if necessary.

FREEZE!

Ideal for freezing in individual portions, ready to defrost for a super-quick lunch.

SCOTCH BROTH

240 calories per portion (if serving 6); 180 calories per portion (if serving 8)

As you diet, you begin to see your ribs again and this hearty soup will stick to them. Some recipes for this gutsy, nourishing Scottish classic use just lamb stock while others include neck fillet or other cuts. Neck is fatty so we use diced lamb leg meat to add flavour and texture to the soup, along with loads of luscious veg and barley. We think it's best to soak the peas overnight, then boil them for ten minutes before adding them to the soup to be on the safe side. You don't want to end up with tough little green bullets in your soup!

Serves 6–8
Prep: 20 minutes, plus soaking time
Cooking time: 1 hour 30 minutes

50g split green peas, soaked
    overnight
400g lean lamb leg meat,
    finely diced
1.2 litres lamb stock or water
50g pearl barley
4 carrots, peeled and finely diced
2 onions, finely diced
2 celery sticks, trimmed and
    finely diced
½ swede, peeled and finely diced
1 large turnip, peeled and finely
    diced
1 sprig of thyme
1 bay leaf
½ cabbage, shredded (white, green
    or savoy)
2 leeks, halved lengthways and
    finely sliced
flaked sea salt
freshly ground black pepper

Soak the split green peas overnight in plenty of water. When you are ready to start making the Scotch broth, drain the peas and put them in a saucepan. Cover with cold water, bring to the boil and boil hard for 10 minutes, then drain and set aside. The peas are now ready to use.

Put the lamb in a large saucepan or casserole dish, cover it with the stock and bring everything to the boil. Skim off any brown foam that collects on the surface and keep doing this until the foam turns white. Add the pearl barley, boiled split peas, carrots, onions, celery, swede, turnips and herbs, then season with salt and pepper and bring back to the boil. Turn the heat down to a low simmer and cook gently for an hour, adding more liquid if necessary.

Add the cabbage and leeks and simmer for another 15 minutes until they are just tender. Serve the Scotch broth in deep bowls.

FREEZE!

Despite containing a lot of vegetables with a high water content, this can be frozen, as the veg are diced very small. Their texture will be slightly affected when defrosted, but it's not as noticeable as it would be if they were cut into large chunks.

BROAD BEAN PILAF

218 calories per portion (if serving 4); 145 calories per portion (if serving 6)
Chicken version: 310 calories per portion (if serving 4); 207 calories (if serving 6)

Dill goes beautifully with broad beans in this lovely comforting rice recipe, which is inspired by a dish we cooked during a very early Hairy Biker trip to Turkey. It's easy to make, but we have to say that unless you have really tiny young beans, it's worth going the extra mile and removing the greyish-green skin that covers each bean. It does make them taste better.

Serves 4 as a main; 6 as a side dish
Prep: 20 minutes, plus marinating time for chicken
Cooking time: about 25 minutes

1 tsp vegetable oil
1 small onion, finely diced
1 small courgette (or half a big one), cut into small dice
1 small piece of cinnamon stick
5 cardamom pods, lightly crushed
1 tsp cumin
½ tsp black pepper
175g basmati rice, well rinsed
300ml vegetable or chicken stock
250g broad beans (fresh or frozen)
a large bunch of parsley, chopped
a small bunch of dill, chopped
flaked sea salt
freshly ground black pepper

Chicken pilaf
ingredients as above, plus
75ml low-fat natural yoghurt
freshly squeezed juice of ½ lemon
a pinch of cinnamon
15g chunk of fresh root ginger, finely grated
4 boneless, skinless chicken thighs, cut into bite-sized pieces

Heat the oil in a saucepan. Add the onion, courgette and spices, then cook over a medium heat for a few minutes until you can smell the wonderful aroma of the spices.

Add the rice and give everything a good stir to make sure the rice is well coated. Pour in the stock and season well with salt. Bring to the boil, then turn down the heat to a gentle simmer, cover the pan and leave for 10 minutes. While the rice is cooking, remove the skins from the beans – this is known as double podding! Using your thumbnail, slit the skin and pop out the bright green bean. Set the beans aside. If you're using frozen beans, defrost them first.

When the rice has been cooking for 10 minutes, add the broad beans. Leave to cook for another 5 minutes, then turn off the heat and leave to stand for 5 minutes. Fluff up the rice with a fork, turning it over gently so the broad beans mix well with everything else. Stir in the herbs, season with salt and pepper if needed and pile the pilaf on to a large serving plate.

Chicken pilaf
Mix together the yoghurt, lemon juice, cinnamon and ginger in a bowl. Season the chicken with salt and pepper, then add the pieces to the marinade in the bowl and leave for an hour.

Follow the recipe as above, but add the chicken, scraped of most of the marinade, just before the rice and stir it for a couple of minutes so it mixes well with the other ingredients and starts to brown slightly. Then add the rice and proceed as before.

CREAMY CHICKEN AND TARRAGON POTS WITH ROSEMARY POTATO WEDGES

chicken: 231 calories per portion; potato wedges: 109 calories per portion

We love that loads of our readers are sending us their own great recipes to try so we decided to hold a competition and print the winner. Here's what Amy Hodgkinson says about her recipe: 'a tasty, tempting pot of creamy deliciousness with all the yum factor of a Great British chicken pie, but none of the calories of puff pastry or double cream'. Congratulations Amy, we totally agree. You'll need some deep ramekins for the chicken pots.

Serves: 3
Prep time: 20 minutes
Cooking time: 40–45 minutes

1 tsp olive oil
2 medium leeks, trimmed and
    sliced into 5mm rings
2 garlic cloves, crushed
3 rashers of lean smoked bacon
2 boneless, skinless chicken breasts
200ml chicken stock
small bunch of fresh tarragon or
    1 tsp dried tarragon
2 tbsp low-fat crème fraiche
30g reduced-fat mature Cheddar
    cheese, grated
freshly ground black pepper

Rosemary-roasted new potato wedges
400g new potatoes
    (about 6 large ones), cut into
    quarters lengthways
1 tsp vegetable oil
a large sprig of rosemary
1 garlic clove, crushed
flaked sea salt
freshly ground black pepper

Place a large non-stick frying pan over a medium heat. Add the olive oil and leek slices and cook for 3 minutes until the leek is starting to soften. Add the crushed garlic and cook for another 2 minutes.

Preheat the oven to 200°C/Fan 180°C/Gas 6. Trim any fat off the bacon and chicken and dice the meat. Add it all to the pan with the leeks, stir and cook over a moderate heat for 5–10 minutes until the chicken is no longer pink. Add the stock to the pan and reduce the heat a little. Cook for 10 minutes until nearly all the stock has reduced and the leeks are completely soft. Turn the heat right down and add the tarragon and crème fraiche, then cook for another 2 minutes. Season with a good grind of pepper.

Spoon the mixture into ramekins and top with the grated cheese. Place the pots on a baking tray and cook in the oven for 15 minutes, until bubbling and golden. Allow to cool for a couple of minutes before serving with green veg and roasted new potato wedges.

Rosemary-roasted new potato wedges
Preheat the oven to 200°C/Fan 180°C/Gas 6 and put a large non-stick baking tray in the oven to heat up. Bring a pan of water to the boil, add the potato wedges and cook for 4 minutes. Drain and put the wedges in a bowl with the oil and rosemary, then season generously. Mix everything together until the potatoes are well coated, then transfer to the heated baking tray in a single layer. Cook for 20 minutes, then add the garlic, give them a good shake around and cook for another 10–15 minutes until golden and crispy.

PASTA WITH CLAMS AND BACON

295 calories per portion

Proper Italian this is, but it's made with tinned clams that you can get in any supermarket. Shellfish and bacon go brilliantly together and using bacon means you don't need much oil. It adds loads of flavour too.

Serves: 4
Prep time: 10 minutes
Cooking time: 10–12 minutes

200g spaghetti
1 tbsp olive oil
2 slices of lean bacon, finely
 chopped
1 shallot or small onion, finely
 chopped
3 garlic cloves, finely chopped
1 tsp chilli flakes (or according
 to taste)
100ml white wine
280g can of clams in brine, drained
2 tbsp chopped flatleaf parsley
flaked sea salt
freshly ground black pepper

Bring a large saucepan of water to the boil. Add the spaghetti, stir well and bring the water back to the boil.Cook the pasta for 10–12 minutes until tender, or according to the packet instructions, stirring occasionally.

While the spaghetti is cooking, heat the oil in a large frying pan over a medium heat. Add the bacon and fry it until crisp and brown. Remove the bacon from the pan and set it aside. Turn the heat down, add the chopped shallot or onion and cook slowly until soft and translucent. Add the garlic and chilli flakes and cook for another 2 minutes, then pour in the wine and simmer for a couple of minutes.

Drain the clams, reserving some of their liquor. Add 50ml of this liquor, along with the clams, to the frying pan, then put the bacon back in the pan. Taste for seasoning and add salt if necessary and a grinding of black pepper.

Drain the pasta in a colander, then tip it into the frying pan. Turn it over so it is all completely covered with the sauce, then serve sprinkled with plenty of parsley.

PASTA WITH SUMMER VEGETABLES AND PARMA HAM

305 calories per portion

This is a deliciously light summery pasta and a welcome change from rich tomato-based sauces. You could use finely sliced runner beans instead of broad beans if you like, and if you leave out the Parma ham this makes an excellent vegetarian dish.

Serves 4
Prep: 20 minutes
Cooking time: 25–30 minutes

75g broad beans (fresh or frozen)
1 tbsp olive oil
1 leek, trimmed and finely sliced
1 garlic clove
2 little gem lettuces, trimmed
   and cut lengthways
100g asparagus spears, cut
   into 4cm lengths
100g peas (fresh or frozen)
1 tbsp fresh tarragon, chopped
50ml white wine
150ml vegetable stock or water
2 tbsp low-fat crème fraîche
200g short pasta, such as farfalle
4 slices of Parma ham
a few leaves of basil, torn
25g Parmesan cheese, grated
flaked sea salt
freshly ground black pepper

Bring a saucepan of water to the boil, add the broad beans and boil them for 1 minute. Remove the pan from the heat, drain the beans and plunge them into a bowl of ice water for a couple of minutes, then drain again. To remove the tough skins from the beans, slit the skin of each one with your thumbnail and pop out the bright green bean. Set the beans aside.

Heat the olive oil in a large saucepan. Add the slices of leek and cook for a few minutes until they're starting to soften. Add the garlic, cook for another minute, then add all the remaining vegetables, and the tarragon, spreading them evenly over the base of the saucepan. Season with salt and black pepper.

Pour in the white wine, let it simmer for a couple of minutes, then add the stock or water. Put the lid on the pan and simmer the veg for about 10 minutes, until the little gems have wilted down. Stir in the crème fraîche and simmer for another couple of minutes.

Meanwhile, bring a large saucepan of water to the boil. Add the pasta, stir well and bring the water back to the boil. Cook the pasta for 10–12 minutes until tender, or according to the packet instructions, stirring occasionally. Drain.

Stir the pasta into the pan with the sauce. Tear the slices of Parma ham into shreds and stir those in, too, with the basil. Sprinkle with the grated Parmesan and serve.

SPAGHETTI WITH PRAWNS AND COURGETTES

250 calories per portion

By popular demand we've included plenty of pasta in this book and this recipe makes us glad we did. It's a super-quick dish that you can put together in not much longer than it takes the spaghetti to cook. There's plenty of great flavours so no need for Parmesan – only adds calories. This doesn't have any sauce as such, and the whole thing is loosened with a ladleful of the cooking liquid. The pasta gives out just enough starch to thicken the water slightly.

Serves 4
Prep: 10 minutes
Cooking time: up to 15 minutes

200g spaghetti
1 tbsp olive oil
1 onion, finely chopped
1 large or 2 medium-sized
    courgettes, diced
2 garlic cloves, finely chopped
freshly grated zest of 1 lemon
2 tbsp capers
200g brown shrimp or cooked,
    peeled North Atlantic prawns,
    defrosted
a fine grating of nutmeg
handful of basil leaves, roughly torn
flaked sea salt
freshly ground black pepper

Bring a large saucepan of water to the boil and add a pinch of salt. Add the spaghetti, stir well and bring the water back to the boil. Cook the pasta for 10–12 minutes until tender, or according to the packet instructions, stirring occasionally.

While the pasta is cooking, heat the olive oil in a large frying pan. Add the onion and courgettes and cook until the onion is soft and the courgettes have started to soften around the edges – you don't want them to break down any more than that. Add the garlic and cook for another couple of minutes, then add the lemon zest and capers and season with lots of black pepper.

When the pasta is done, drain it in a colander, reserving a jugful of the cooking liquid. Add the shrimp or prawns to the frying pan, then a small ladleful of the pasta cooking liquid. Grate over a little nutmeg. Allow the sauce to bubble for a few moments, then add the pasta and the basil. Turn everything over so it is all thoroughly combined. If the dish seems too dry, add a little more cooking liquid. Serve immediately.

IRISH STEW

500 calories per portion

A traditional Irish stew is made with lamb on the bone or neck fillet, but neck is very fatty, so is high in calories. We prefer double chops – Barnsley chops – or leg steaks, which are fairly lean, and using meat on the bone gives extra flavour. The marrow helps the texture of the dish too. One thing you can do to reduce the fat – and calorie count – if you have time, is to cook the dish the night before up to the point of adding the potatoes, then chill. The next day, skim off the fat, which will have solidified, then reheat and add the potatoes as below.

Serves 4 generously
Prep: 20 minutes
Cooking time: 1 hour
20–30 minutes

4 Barnsley chops or leg steaks
1 tbsp oil
2 large onions, sliced
4 large carrots, peeled and sliced
    widthways on the diagonal
2 bay leaves
a sprig of thyme
a sprig of parsley
750ml–1 litre lamb or chicken
    stock, to cover
600g potatoes, peeled and
    thickly sliced
2 tbsp chopped parsley, to serve
    (optional)
flaked sea salt
freshly ground black pepper

Trim the meat of any excess fat. If using chops, you can also pull off the skin if you like, as there will be some fat just under it.

Heat the oil in a large casserole dish. Add the lamb and brown it well on both sides. Remove the lamb from the dish and add the onions and carrots. Cook, while stirring, for a couple of minutes, then add the herbs and put the lamb back in the dish. Pour in the stock, making sure the lamb and vegetables are just covered, and season with salt and pepper.

Cover the casserole dish and bring the stew to the boil, then turn the heat down and simmer for about 45 minutes. By this time the lamb should be well on its way to being tender. Add the potato slices in a layer on the top and simmer until they are tender and starting to break down – this should take about 20 minutes. Sprinkle with parsley before serving if you like.

FREEZE!

If you want to freeze this stew, prepare it up to and including the stage of simmering for 45 minutes, then cool and freeze. When you want to use it, defrost and reheat gently, then add the potatoes and finish cooking as above.

MINCED BEEF PLATE PIE

439 calories per portion (if serving 4); 351 calories per portion (if serving 5); 293 calories per portion (if serving 6)

One thing we're really pleased about is that we've managed to lose weight while still enjoying our favourite foods – such as pies. Surprisingly, potatoes contain fewer calories than flour so by using some mash in this pastry you can also include butter, which gives it great taste and texture. We call this a 'cut and come again pie', but beware of making too many visits if you want to stay sylphlike.

Serves 4–6
Prep: 30 minutes, plus chilling time for pastry
Cooking time: about 1 hour 15 minutes

Filling
250g lean beef mince
2 onions, sliced
2 carrots, peeled and cut into small dice
100g swede, peeled weight, cut into small dice
2 celery sticks, trimmed and diced
400g can of brown lentils, drained
1 tsp dried oregano
1 tsp finely chopped thyme
1 tbsp anchovy paste (optional)
1 tbsp tomato purée
300ml beef stock
flaked sea salt
freshly ground black pepper

Pastry
275g floury potatoes, preferably Maris Pipers or King Edwards
40g chilled butter, diced
80g plain flour
1–2 tbsp semi-skimmed milk
1 egg, lightly beaten, to glaze
pinch of salt

Make the pastry as for our steak and kidney pie on pages 98–99. Wrap it in cling film and leave it to chill for at least half an hour.

Meanwhile, make the filling, put the mince, onions, carrots, swede and celery in a large frying pan. Dry-fry, stirring constantly until the beef has browned and make sure you break up any clumps of meat. Add the lentils, herbs, anchovy paste (if using), tomato purée and stock. Stir to mix everything well, then bring to the boil and season with salt and pepper. Cover the pan and simmer for about 20 minutes or until the vegetables have softened. Set aside to cool.

Preheat the oven to 200°C/Fan 180°C/Gas 6. Tip the filling into a round pie plate or dish. Roll the pastry out on a lightly floured work surface until it is large enough to cover your pie plate. It will be fairly thin, about 3mm, but should be robust enough not to break when you lift it.

Wet the rim of the pie plate with water. Carefully lift the pastry using the rolling pin and place it over the pie, pressing the edges firmly around the rim. For a good colour, glaze the pie with some lightly beaten egg.

Bake in the preheated oven for 40–45 minutes until the pastry is cooked and a lovely golden colour. Serve with some freshly cooked green vegetables.

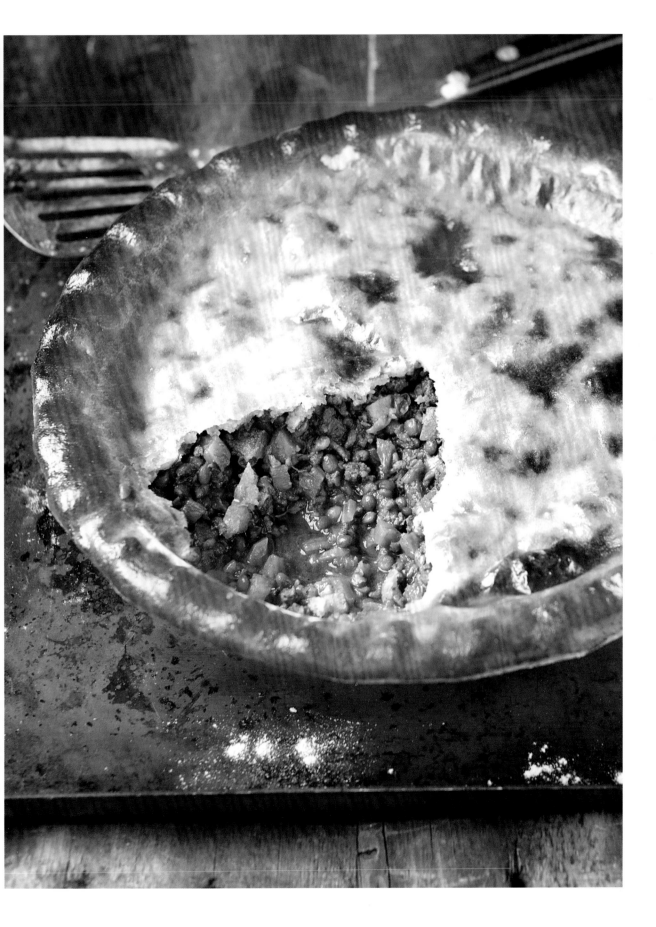

VEGGIE WONDERS

We love our vegetables and we've learned that they can be the stars of the show – not just something to add a bit of colour on the plate. Recipes like our aubergine bake and Greek roast vegetables can be a meal in themselves, as well as going beautifully with some grilled meat or chicken. We've also come up with some deliciously hearty salads, such as our versions of Middle Eastern tabbouleh and fattoush, that will really tickle your taste buds.

AUBERGINE BAKE

205 calories per portion (with one ball of mozzarella); 269 calories with two balls

Our low-cal version of an Italian classic – melanzane parmigiana – makes a comforting veggie supper dish. Aubergines are low in calories, despite their chunky, meaty feel, but the dish usually contains lots of oil. We've cut right back on the oil but there's still plenty of tasty sauce. Use one or two balls of mozzarella as you like, but remember that more mozz means more calories.

Serves 4
Prep: 15–20 minutes
Cooking time: 1 hour 15 minutes
(if cooking aubergines in 1 batch)

4 large aubergines,
    sliced into 1cm rounds
oil, for spraying
a handful of basil leaves,
    roughly torn
1 or 2 balls of half-fat mozzarella

Tomato sauce
1 tbsp olive oil
1 onion, finely chopped
2 cloves garlic, finely chopped
1 tsp oregano
small pinch of cinnamon
small pinch of sugar
200ml red wine
2 x 400g cans of chopped tomatoes
flaked sea salt
freshly ground black pepper

Preheat the oven to 200°C/Fan 180°C/Gas 6. You may need to cook the aubergines in a couple of batches. Line 2 large baking trays with non-stick baking parchment. Arrange the slices of aubergine on the trays, then mist them very lightly with oil – you will probably need about 3 sprays per tray.

Put the trays in the oven and roast the aubergine slices until they are soft and the flesh is golden brown in patches. This will take about 40–45 minutes. Remove the aubergines from the oven and set them aside to cool while you cook the rest of the slices in the same way.

Meanwhile make the tomato sauce. Heat the olive oil in a large saucepan. Add the onion and fry over a low heat until soft and translucent. Add the garlic and cook for another 2 minutes. Sprinkle over the oregano, cinnamon and sugar and give everything a quick stir. Pour in the red wine and turn up the heat, then simmer quite briskly until the liquid has reduced by about half. Add the tomatoes and season with salt and pepper, then simmer for at least 20 minutes, until the sauce has reduced and thickened.

Take a large ovenproof baking dish and spread a little of the tomato sauce on the bottom. Cover with a layer of aubergines and some roughly torn basil, then continue adding layers of sauce and aubergines until you have used everything up – you should have at least 3 layers of aubergines. Finish with a thin layer of tomato sauce. Slice the mozzarella as thinly as you can and arrange it over the aubergines and sauce. It doesn't matter if there are gaps, it will spread a little during cooking. Put the dish in the oven and bake for 30 minutes until the aubergines are very tender and the mozzarella has melted and browned a little. Serve with a green salad.

TABBOULEH

101 calories per portion (if serving 4); 68 calories per portion (if serving 6)

An authentic tabbouleh contains very little bulgur wheat but lots and lots of herbs, and ours is no exception. This is great on its own, with a group of other salad dishes or with some grilled chicken. The celeriac adds extra texture, but if you don't like it – or can't get hold of any – just use an extra courgette.

Serves 4–6
Prep: 15 minutes, plus
20 minutes soaking time

1 red onion, finely chopped
30g bulgur wheat
100g celeriac, peeled
2 courgettes
200g large, ripe red tomatoes, finely chopped
1 red pepper, deseeded and finely diced
a large bunch of flatleaf parsley, finely sliced (not chopped)
a small bunch of mint, leaves only, finely sliced
flaked sea salt

Dressing
1 tbsp olive oil
juice of 1 lemon
pinch of cinnamon
1 tsp ground cumin
flaked sea salt
freshly ground black pepper

Put the finely chopped red onion in a bowl, sprinkle with some salt and cover with cold water. Leave to stand for 20 minutes. This takes the harshness out of the onions and makes the flavour more mellow. Soak the bulgur wheat in a bowl of just-boiled water for 5 minutes, then drain and set aside.

Cut the celeriac into chunks. Top and tail the courgettes and cut them into chunks too. Put the celeriac in a food processor and pulse a few times, then add the courgettes and pulse again until everything is the size of large breadcrumbs.

Drain the onion and put it in a bowl with the celeriac, courgettes, tomatoes and pepper, then stir in the herbs. Whisk all the dressing ingredients together and pour over the vegetables. Stir, then leave to stand for a few minutes before eating. This salad is best served at room temperature.

FATTOUSH

163 calories per portion

Eat fattoush for a slim tush! Seriously, though, this is a classic Middle Eastern salad that contains toasted pitta bread to give it a bit more oomph. Sumac, a beautifully tart spice, adds a real punch of flavour and you can find it in most supermarkets now. If you don't have any, the dish will still taste good.

Serves 4
Prep: 15 minutes
Cooking time: 10–15 minutes

2 pitta breads
250g cherry tomatoes, halved
1 large cucumber, diced
2 large or 4 small little gem
    lettuces, cut widthways
    into strips
1 large green pepper, deseeded
    and diced
4 spring onions, sliced into rounds
200g radishes, sliced into rounds
a small bunch of flatleaf parsley,
    finely chopped
a small bunch of mint,
    finely chopped

Dressing
freshly squeezed juice of 1 lemon
1 tbsp olive oil
1 tsp sumac (optional), plus extra
    for sprinkling
pinch of cinnamon
flaked sea salt
freshly ground black pepper

Preheat the oven to 220°C/Fan 200°C/Gas 7.

Cut down the sides of the pitta breads and split them in half so you have 4 thin flatbreads. Put these on a baking tray and bake in the preheated oven until they're crisp and starting to turn golden brown. This should take 10–15 minutes. Remove the pittas from the oven and when they're cool enough to handle – this won't take long at all – tear them into small pieces.

Put the rest of the salad ingredients into a large bowl, add the torn pieces of pitta bread and mix thoroughly.

Whisk together the dressing ingredients and pour the whole lot over the salad. Mix thoroughly with salad spoons or, better still, with your hands.

Serve in large shallow bowls, with a little more sumac sprinkled over the top if you like.

QUINOA SALAD

212 calories per portion

We've been quite bossy about how to put this salad together so you can enjoy it at its fabulous best. If you just mix it all up it will look messy – although it will still be good to eat. If your asparagus is really fresh you can leave it raw for some crunch. Alternatively, you can blanch it briefly or put it on a hot griddle for a few moments for some decorative charring.

Serves 4
Prep: 15 minutes
Cooking time: about 15 minutes

75g quinoa, washed and drained
pinch of salt
8 asparagus spears
2 oranges
100g bag of watercress and spinach
 leaves (or similar)
1 ripe avocado, peeled and cut
 into small chunks
4 spring onions, cut into rounds
leaves from a small bunch of mint

Dressing
1 tbsp olive oil
freshly squeezed juice of 1 lime
1 tbsp soy sauce
½ tsp caster sugar
1 garlic clove, crushed
1 hot red chilli, deseeded and
 finely chopped
flaked sea salt
freshly ground black pepper

To cook the quinoa, tip it into a saucepan with double the volume of water (150ml). Add a pinch of salt and bring to the boil, then cover and turn down the heat. Simmer the quinoa until the water has been absorbed – about 15 minutes. Remove the pan from the heat and leave the quinoa to cool.

Bend each asparagus spear until it snaps and discard the woody end. If you're serving the asparagus raw, simply slice the spears on the diagonal, as thinly as you can, leaving the tips whole. If you prefer your asparagus cooked, blanch or griddle the spears until tender and then slice them thinly.

Peel the oranges and divide them into segments – do this over the bowl you intend making the salad dressing in, so you catch any juice. Set the segments aside and add the rest of the dressing ingredients to the bowl with the juice and whisk them together.

Wash the salad leaves and arrange them on a platter or individual salad plates. Sprinkle over most of the quinoa and spoon over some of the dressing Add the asparagus spears, avocado, orange segments, spring onions and mint leaves. Sprinkle over the rest of the quinoa and pour over the remaining dressing. Toss everything very lightly just before serving.

ROOT VEGETABLE BOULANGÈRE

127 calories per portion (if serving 4); 85 calories per portion (if serving 6)

A lovely comforting dish, this was traditionally made just with potatoes and cooked in the baker's oven. Our version uses parsnips and carrots instead of all potatoes to keep the calorie count down and give extra flavour. It's good on its own or goes well with grilled meat.

Serves 4–6
Prep: 10 minutes
Cooking time: about 1 hour

1 large or 2 small parsnips, peeled (about 300g peeled weight)
2 large carrots, peeled (about 250g peeled weight)
2 large potatoes, King Edwards are good (about 400g peeled weight)
oil, for spraying
1 tsp dried sage
2 garlic cloves, finely chopped
600ml vegetable or chicken stock
flaked sea salt
freshly ground black pepper

Preheat the oven to 200°C/Fan 180°C/Gas 6.

Prepare the vegetables. If the parsnips are fat enough, cut them into rounds, otherwise slice into lengths, as thinly as possible. The carrots should also be sliced thinly, but on the diagonal. Finally, cut the potatoes into slightly thicker slices – about 2–3mm.

Spray a baking dish lightly with oil. Arrange the parsnips over the base – you should have enough for at least 2 layers, perhaps 3 if you have managed to slice them very thinly. Follow with half the sage and garlic, then season lightly with salt and pepper.

Add a layer of carrots, then repeat the sage, garlic and seasoning. Finally, top with the potatoes.

Make up the stock with boiling water, or heat gently if using fresh stock, and pour this over the vegetables. Cover the baking dish with a single layer of foil and bake in the preheated oven for half an hour. Uncover the baking dish and cook for another half an hour or until the vegetables are tender and most of the liquid has evaporated.

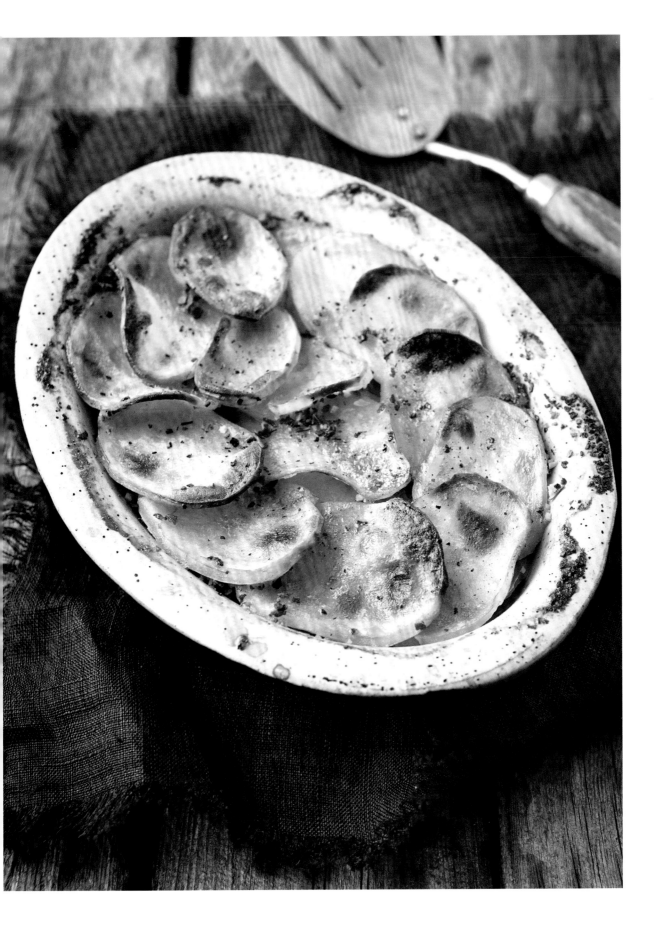

RED CABBAGE WITH APPLE AND CHESTNUTS

76 calories per portion

Serves 8
Prep: 10 minutes
Cooking time: 25–30 minutes

---

1 tbsp vegetable oil
1 onion, finely chopped
2 garlic cloves, finely chopped
2 eating apples, peeled and grated
    or finely chopped
1 small red cabbage, quartered,
    cored and shredded
a pinch of cinnamon
½ tsp allspice
1 tsp brown sugar
100g vacuum-packed chestnuts,
    roughly chopped
1 tbsp cider vinegar
flaked sea salt
freshly ground black pepper

Many red cabbage recipes need a long cooking time and contain quite a bit of sugar. We've cut down on both here and the result is quick and delicious – and the cabbage keeps its colour. The recipe does make quite a large quantity but freezes brilliantly, so stash some away for another meal if you don't need it all. For a variation, you could use some diced bacon instead of the vinegar and sugar.

Heat the oil in a large saucepan. Add the onion and cook for a few minutes until soft, then add the garlic and cook for another 2 minutes. Now add the apples and cabbage, season with salt and pepper, then sprinkle over the cinnamon, allspice and sugar. Add the chestnuts. Stir the cider vinegar into 100ml of water and pour this into the pan.

Cover and simmer for about 20 minutes until the red cabbage has softened slightly but still has its deep colour.

SPRING GREENS WITH HARISSA AND GARLIC

41 calories per portion

Serves 4
Prep: 5 minutes
Cooking time: 5–8 minutes

---

1 tsp olive oil
2 garlic cloves, finely chopped
1 tsp–1 tbsp harissa paste, to taste
400g bag of spring greens, washed
    and finely shredded
freshly grated zest of 1 lemon
flaked sea salt
freshly ground black pepper

Make this as hot or not as you like. A teaspoon of harissa gives a mellow heat while a tablespoon packs more of a punch – up to you.

Heat the olive oil in a large frying pan or saucepan with a lid. Add the garlic cloves and harissa paste and cook for a couple of minutes, stirring constantly.

Add 100ml of water and stir to combine with the garlic and paste, then add the greens. Turn the greens over so they are coated with the sauce, then season with salt and pepper. Cover and cook on a medium heat for about 5 minutes, stirring every so often, until the spring greens have wilted, but still have a little bite to them. Add the lemon zest at the last minute.

GREEK-STYLE ROAST VEGETABLES

176 calories per portion (if serving 4); 117 calories per portion (if serving 6)

This kind of one-pot vegetable dish usually contains loads of olive oil and so is high in calories. We've found that you can get away with just a small amount of oil and loads of juicy veg and it still tastes fantastic. The veg are good cold too, so make extra and use in a salad.

Serves 4–6
Prep: 15 minutes
Cooking time: 1 hour

300g potatoes, unpeeled and sliced
   into rounds
2 large courgettes, sliced into
   rounds
2 red onions, peeled and cut into
   thin wedges
2 peppers (red or green) cut into
   chunks
a few garlic cloves, unpeeled
1 tsp dried oregano or mixed herbs
1 tbsp olive oil
100ml white wine
300ml vegetable stock, chicken
   stock or water
12 cherry tomatoes
flaked sea salt
freshly ground black pepper

Preheat the oven to 200°C/Fan 180°C/Gas 6.

Put all the vegetables and garlic in a large roasting tin or shallow casserole dish. Sprinkle over the herbs and season well with salt and pepper. Drizzle over the olive oil, then mix everything together with your hands so all the vegetables have a coating of oil.

Mix the wine and stock or water and pour over the vegetables. Either cover your roasting tin with foil or put the lid on your casserole dish, then place in the preheated oven for half an hour.

Remove the foil or lid and gently turn everything over with a spoon. Dot the cherry tomatoes around the dish, then put it back in the oven for another half an hour, uncovered, until most of the liquid has evaporated and the vegetables have started to brown.

ROASTED CARROT, PEPPER AND CHICKPEA SALAD

136 calories per portion

You can make the zingy dressing for this salad with orange or lemon, but we like to add a pinch of caster sugar or a little drizzle of honey if using lemon. With orange, add a tiny squeeze of lemon juice. The salad can be served on its own with some leaves or to accompany some plain grilled meat.

Serves 4
Prep: 20 minutes
Cooking time: 35 minutes

2 large carrots, peeled and cut
   into 2cm chunks
1 tsp ground cumin
1 tsp olive oil
2 red peppers, deseeded and cut
   in half, lengthways
400g can of chickpeas, drained
   and rinsed
2 tbsp chopped dill
2 tbsp chopped mint
2 tbsp chopped parsley or coriander
flaked sea salt
freshly ground black pepper

Dressing
1 tsp tahini
1 tsp olive oil
freshly squeezed juice of 1 orange
   or lemon
1 garlic clove, crushed
¼ tsp allspice
½ tsp cumin
pinch of caster sugar or small
   drizzle of honey (optional)

Preheat the oven to 220°C/Fan 200°C/Gas 7. Line a roasting dish with baking parchment.

Bring a saucepan of water to the boil. Add a pinch of salt and the carrots and simmer for 15 minutes until they're almost tender. Drain the carrots and tip them into the roasting dish, then season with salt, pepper and cumin. Drizzle with the olive oil.

Push the carrots into one half of the roasting dish and put the peppers in the other half, cut side down. Roast for 20 minutes until the carrots have taken on some colour and the peppers are starting to soften and look slightly charred. Remove the dish from the oven and put the peppers in a bag or a covered bowl and leave them to steam until they are cool enough to handle. Peel off the skin – it should come off easily – and cut or tear the peppers into thin strips.

To make the dressing, whisk all the ingredients together and season with salt and pepper. If using lemon juice, you might like to add a pinch of caster sugar or a little drizzle of honey.

To assemble the salad, put the carrots, peppers and chickpeas in a large bowl. Add all the herbs, then pour over the dressing. Mix everything together, then leave to stand at room temperature for a while to let the flavours develop before serving.

SUNSHINE FOOD

We both love Mediterranean-style and Middle Eastern food, with all those great flavours of herbs, spices and wonderful veg. And, of course, we discovered that if you cut down on the oil a bit, these sunshine dishes can be healthy, low-cal eating as well as good eating. Try our recipes for Italian ribollita and Moroccan harira soups – both a meal in themselves. Or cook up some souvlaki or lamb burgers and tzatziki, put your sunnies on and imagine yourself on a terrace overlooking the Med – maybe even in that new swimsuit you can now wear with pride!

BEAN AND VEGETABLE SOUP

290 calories per portion

Our version of ribollita, a classic Italian recipe, this is a good hearty soup. We've used less pasta than usual, but there are plenty of beans and veg. Use any sort of cabbage you like, including spring greens, kale or Swiss chard, but don't be tempted to try spinach — it will just end up as mush. This is also a great recipe for using up a bit of Parmesan rind if you have one in the fridge — provides some extra punch and flavour.

Serves 4
Prep: 15 minutes
Cooking time: about 40 minutes

1 tbsp olive oil
50g back bacon, trimmed of fat
   and finely diced
1 onion, finely chopped
1 fennel bulb, trimmed and
   finely chopped
2 carrots, finely chopped
2 celery sticks, chopped
4 garlic cloves, finely chopped
1 tsp dried oregano
a Parmesan rind (optional)
100ml red wine
400g can of cannellini beans,
   drained and rinsed
4 fresh tomatoes, finely chopped, or
   200g canned chopped tomatoes
600ml chicken stock
50g pasta (any short form will do)
½ green cabbage or the equivalent
   in other greens
1 large courgette, diagonally sliced
squeeze of lemon juice (optional)
flaked sea salt
freshly ground black pepper

To serve
handful of basil leaves, roughly torn
25g Parmesan cheese, grated

Heat the olive oil in a large saucepan or casserole dish. Add the diced bacon and fry until crisp and brown. Add the onion, fennel, carrots, celery and garlic and sauté for a couple of minutes. Sprinkle over the oregano, add the Parmesan rind, if using, then pour over the red wine. Bring to the boil and simmer until the wine has reduced by about half.

Add the beans and tomatoes, then pour in the stock. Bring the soup back to the boil and simmer for about 15 minutes until all the vegetables are tender. Add the pasta and cabbage, continue to simmer for 5 minutes, then add the courgette. Simmer for another 5–10 minutes until the pasta is cooked al dente and all the vegetables are cooked through. Check for seasoning and if you think the soup needs it, add a squeeze of lemon juice.

Sprinkle over the basil and serve with a scant tablespoon each of grated Parmesan.

FREEZE!

This freezes well but best to add the courgette after defrosting.

SPICY MOROCCAN SOUP

330 calories per portion (if serving 4); 220 calories per portion (if serving 6)

This is our quick way of making a Moroccan soup known as harira, which is the traditional way to break your fast at Ramadan. It's fragrant, spicy and very nourishing and doesn't take long to make. If you don't have all the spices you could use a spice blend such as ras-el-hanout or harissa instead. Both are available in supermarkets.

Serves 4–6
Prep: 15 minutes
Cooking time: 1 hour 15 minutes

1 tbsp olive oil
2 onions, sliced
2 peppers (1 red, 1 green),
    deseeded and cut into strips
250g lamb, preferably leg meat,
    finely diced into ½–1cm cubes
1 tsp turmeric
1 tsp ground ginger
1 tsp ground coriander
2 tsp ground cumin
½ tsp cinnamon
½ tsp hot chilli powder
1 pinch of saffron strands
1 garlic clove
1 litre chicken stock or water
400g can of tomatoes
2 tbsp chopped fresh coriander,
    plus extra for serving
2 tbsp chopped flatleaf parsley, plus
    extra for serving
400g can of chickpeas, drained
    and rinsed
50g long-grain rice
freshly squeezed juice of ½ lemon
flaked sea salt
freshly ground black pepper

Heat the olive oil in a large saucepan. Add the onions and peppers and cook for a few minutes over a low to medium heat until they start to soften. Turn up the heat, add the lamb and brown it quickly on all sides.

Turn the heat down again and add all the spices (or the spice blend, if using) and the garlic. Sauté for a couple more minutes until everything is well combined, then pour in the stock. Season with salt and freshly ground black pepper. Bring to the boil, then turn the heat down and leave the soup to simmer for 30 minutes.

Put the tomatoes in a blender with 2 tablespoons each of coriander and parsley and blitz until the herbs are very finely chopped. Pour this mixture into the saucepan, then add the chickpeas and rice. Simmer for another 30 minutes, by which time the meat should be beautifully tender.

Just before serving, stir in the lemon juice and taste for seasoning, then adjust if necessary. Sprinkle with extra chopped coriander and parsley and serve.

FREEZE!

Freezes very well. It's best to add the lemon juice after defrosting as certain flavours – garlic and ginger in particular – intensify on freezing and you might not need it. Taste first and add lemon if you think it's necessary.

MACKEREL FILLETS WITH GREMOLATA

339 calories per portion;

Gremolata is the name for a simple but tasty Italian garnish. It's just finely chopped garlic, parsley and lemon zest but it adds a fantastic zingy flavour to chicken, meat or fish, such as this super-speedy mackerel dish. We've suggested cooking the fish in a frying pan with just a light spritz of oil, but you could also do it on a griddle or a barbecue – with one of those fish cages. Lovely served with a tomato and onion salad if you fancy.

Serves 2
Prep: 10 minutes
Cooking time: 5 minutes

oil, for spraying
4 small mackerel fillets,
    about 300g in total
2 tbsp finely chopped flatleaf
    parsley
2 garlic cloves, finely chopped
finely grated zest of 1 lemon
flaked sea salt
freshly ground black pepper

Tomato and onion salad
1 small sweet white onion, finely
    sliced into crescents
2 or 3 very ripe vine tomatoes
1 tsp olive oil
squeeze of lemon juice
a pinch of sugar
1 tbsp finely chopped flatleaf
    parsley
1 tsp salted capers, rinsed (optional)
flaked sea salt
finely ground white pepper

Lightly spray a large non-stick frying pan with oil and place it over a medium heat. Season the mackerel fillets with salt and pepper. Put the fillets in the pan, skin-side down, and cook for 3–4 minutes. When the flesh of the mackerel is almost completely white and opaque, turn the fillets over and cook for another minute.

Mix the parsley, garlic and lemon zest together to make the gremolata. Serve the mackerel with the gremolata on the side, for sprinkling over.

Tomato and onion salad
Soaking onions before using them raw takes off that really astringent edge. But again, if you don't mind that, you can leave out the soaking step.

Sprinkle salt over the onion slices and put them in a bowl of very cold water. Leave for 10 minutes, then drain. Slice the tomatoes horizontally into thin rounds and arrange them on a plate. Sprinkle over the onion crescents.

Whisk together the olive oil, lemon juice, sugar, salt and white pepper. Pour this over the tomatoes and onions. Sprinkle over the parsley and the capers, if using. Leave for a few minutes to allow the flavours to develop, then serve at room temperature.

CHICKEN CACCIATORE

281 calories per portion

This is an old-fashioned dish but one that's very popular with the 18–30s – we mean age here, not dress size. It's great just as it is but you can also add some thinly sliced veg, such as red peppers and celery, if you like.

Serves 4
Prep: 15 minutes
Cooking time: about 1 hour
15 minutes

—————

1 tbsp olive oil
2 onions, finely sliced
4 garlic cloves, finely chopped
a large sprig of rosemary
4 bone-in chicken thighs, skinned,
4 chicken drumsticks, skinned
150ml white wine
150ml chicken stock
200g fresh tomatoes, peeled and
    deseeded and chopped, or 200g
    canned chopped tomatoes
handful of flatleaf parsley, chopped
flaked sea salt
freshly ground black pepper

Heat the olive oil in a large casserole dish on the hob. Add the onions and cook them over a low heat until they are soft and translucent – this should take about 15 minutes. Add the garlic and rosemary and cook for another couple of minutes.

Turn the heat up, push the onions to one side and add the chicken pieces. Fry them, turning the pieces over once or twice until they are very lightly browned, then mix with the onions.

Pour in the white wine and allow it to bubble down. Add the chicken stock and tomatoes, then season with salt and pepper. Turn the heat down, cover the dish and leave to simmer gently for about 45 minutes until the chicken is cooked through and very tender. Sprinkle with chopped parsley and serve with some green veg.

FREEZE!

This freezes well. To use, defrost thoroughly and reheat gently, adding a little more liquid if necessary. Stir as little as possible while reheating so you don't break up the chicken too much.

LAMB BURGERS WITH TZATZIKI

385 calories per portion (if serving 4);
257 calories per portion (if serving 6)

Flavoured with chopped herbs and lemon zest, these burgers have a real Mediterranean zing.

Serves 4–6
Prep: 20 minutes
Cooking time: 12–15 minutes

1 tsp olive oil
1 onion, finely chopped
2 garlic cloves, finely chopped
500g lean lamb mince
50g breadcrumbs
2 tsp dried mint
1 tsp dried oregano
1 tsp finely chopped rosemary
zest of 1 lemon
small pinch of cinnamon
50g low-fat natural yoghurt
flaked sea salt
freshly ground black pepper

Tzatziki
1 large cucumber
250g low-fat natural yoghurt
2 garlic cloves, crushed
1 tsp white wine vinegar
2 tsp dried mint

FREEZE!

The burgers/balls freeze well, raw or cooked. Open freeze them on a baking tray, then when solid, put in bags to store. Don't try to freeze the tzatziki!

Preheat the oven to 220°C/Fan 200°C/Gas 7. Line a baking tray with baking parchment.

Heat the oil in a frying pan. Add the chopped onion and cook, stirring regularly, until it's soft and translucent. Add the garlic cloves and cook for another 2 minutes. Remove the pan from the heat and allow the onion and garlic to cool.

Put the lamb in a bowl and break up any clumps. Season generously with salt and pepper and sprinkle over the breadcrumbs, herbs, lemon zest and cinnamon. Add the onions and garlic, along with the yoghurt, and mix the whole lot together. The easiest way to do this is with your hands. Divide the mixture into 6 portions and form burger-sized patties. Alternatively, if you prefer meatballs, shape them into balls the size of a golf ball – about 40g each.

Space the burgers or balls on the baking tray. Bake them in the oven for 12–15 minutes, until well browned. If you want the lamb slightly pink in the middle, cook for 10 minutes. Serve with tzatziki.

Tzatziki
Peel the cucumber and cut it in half lengthways. Scoop out the seeds with a teaspoon and discard. Coarsely grate the cucumber and put it in a colander. Sprinkle it with salt and leave over a bowl or in the sink to drain for half an hour.

After half an hour, wring out as much water from the cucumber as you can. A good way to do this is to put it all on a clean tea towel, scrunch the tea towel up into a bundle and twist the edges together, then squeeze hard! You'll be amazed at how much water comes out. Put the yoghurt in a bowl and add the garlic, white wine vinegar and mint. Add the cucumber and stir well.

PORK SOUVLAKI WITH LIGHT SALSA VERDE

270 calories per portion (if serving 4);
180 calories per portion (if serving 6)

These pork kebabs are satisfaction on a stick. Salsa verde goes beautifully with them but usually contains shedloads of olive oil. We've come up with something that's more like a herby mayonnaise and we really love it – see what you think.

Serves 4–6
Prep: 15 minutes,
plus marinating
Cooking time: 12–15 minutes

700g lean pork, diced into
    3cm chunks

Marinade
1 tsp olive oil
juice of 1 lemon
1 tsp dried mint
1 tsp dried oregano
1 bay leaf, crumbled
1 tbsp red wine vinegar
flaked sea salt
freshly ground black pepper

Light salsa verde
1 egg yolk
1 heaped tsp Dijon mustard
1 tbsp olive oil
juice of 1 lemon
2 anchovies, finely chopped
    (optional)
2 tbsp capers, rinsed and chopped
a large bunch of flatleaf parsley
    leaves, finely chopped
a small bunch of basil, finely
    chopped
a small bunch of mint, finely
    chopped
flaked sea salt
freshly ground black pepper

Mix all the marinade ingredients together in a large non-metallic bowl. Add the pork and stir until it's all completely covered, then leave to marinate in the fridge for at least half an hour – it's fine to leave it overnight if that suits you.

If you're using bamboo skewers, soak them in water for half an hour before you need them – this will prevent them from burning. Thread the pork chunks on to 8 skewers. Cook the souvlaki on a hot barbecue, on a griddle pan on the hob (you may have to do this in batches) or under a hot grill, for 12–15 minutes. Turn the skewers regularly, until all the meat is charred and cooked through.

Serve the pork kebabs on or off the skewers, with the sauce on the side; nice with a simple tomato and onion salad (see page 146).

Light salsa verde
Put the egg yolk in a bowl with the mustard. Whisk them together, then add the olive oil, a few drops at a time so the mixture emulsifies properly. Whisk in the lemon juice, then stir in all the remaining ingredients. If you want a very smooth sauce, blitz it briefly in a blender. You can also add a tablespoon of water if you prefer the sauce slightly thinner.

PORK SALTIMBOCCA

194 calories per portion

We watched Antonio Carluccio cook this fab Italian dish and couldn't wait to try it ourselves. It usually contains quite a bit of butter, but we've taken that out and kept the lovely tasty ham and sage so it's really good to eat. You can reduce the calorie count by removing the fat from the ham, but we like to leave it on for extra flavour.

Serves 4
Prep: 15 minutes
Cooking time: about 10 minutes

4 small medallions of pork fillet
    or loin, about 100g each
4 slices of Parma ham
2 tsp dried sage
finely grated zest of 1 lemon
2 tsp olive oil
100ml Marsala wine (or you could
    use medium sherry)
50ml chicken stock or water
squeeze of lemon juice
freshly ground black pepper

Put a pork medallion between 2 large sheets of cling film. Flatten it with a rolling pin or the smooth side of a meat mallet until you have a very thin escalope – about ½ cm. Repeat with the remaining pieces of pork.

Sprinkle each escalope with dried sage and lemon zest, then season with pepper – not salt, as the ham is salty enough. Top with a slice of Parma ham and press it down firmly. If any edges of the ham overlap the pork, just tuck them underneath.

Heat 1 teaspoon of the olive oil in a large frying pan. Fry 2 of the pork escalopes at a time – they will only need 2 minutes on each side. You should find that the Parma ham will stick to the escalope without any problem. Transfer the escalopes to a plate and keep them warm while you cook the rest. If the frying pan seems a bit dry, add the second teaspoon of olive oil.

Pour the Marsala into the frying pan and allow it to bubble up while you scrape any sticky bits off the bottom of the pan, then add the water or stock. Simmer for a couple of minutes to reduce – you want a sauce with the consistency of a very light syrup. Drain off any juice that may have come from the resting escalopes and add this to the sauce, together with a squeeze of lemon juice. Serve the escalopes with the sauce spooned over and perhaps a salad, such as our fattoush (see page 128).

SANDWICHES, DIPS AND SNACKS

Diet or no diet, we all need a quick satisfying snack from time to time and we're constantly asked what we do about food on the move. It's true that we have to think a bit to stay out of trouble but we're getting better at it. Our latest dip recipes can be eaten straight from the fridge with crunchy veg sticks when you come home starving, or made into open sandwiches or wraps for a light meal or to pop in your lunch box. The pad Thai omelette was inspired by the street food we enjoyed in Thailand and the cauliflower nuggets taste like a naughty bar snack but come in at under 100 calories a portion. Can't say fairer than that.

POTATO BREAD

about 65 calories per slice, cut into 20 slices

We first came across potato bread in Germany when we were working on our
Big Book of Baking. You might be surprised to hear this, but replacing some
of the flour in bread with mashed potato cuts the calories! Strange but true.
You'll love this bread and it's brilliant for sandwiches.

Makes 1 loaf
Prep: 25 minutes, plus proving time
Cooking time: 30 minutes

375g potatoes, preferably Maris
   Pipers or King Edwards
oil, for spraying
1 sachet (about 7g) of fast-acting
   dried yeast
1 tsp sugar
1 tsp salt
300g strong white flour
75ml warm water

FREEZE!

Freezes well. You can slice
the loaf before freezing –
should get about 20 slices
– and then take them out
of the freezer as you need.
The bread is best toasted
after freezing.

First, make the mash so it can cool down before you use it. Peel the potatoes and cut them into chunks of about 3cm. Put them in a large saucepan, cover with cold water and bring to the boil. Cook for 10–15 minutes or until very tender – test them with the tip of a knife. Drain the potatoes in a large colander and tip them back into the saucepan, then mash until smooth – don't add any butter or milk. Leave the mash to cool but it doesn't have to be stone cold before using. Lightly spray a 2lb loaf tin with oil.

Put 300g of the mashed potato in a large bowl and sprinkle over the yeast and sugar. Give it a quick mix so the yeast isn't all on the surface of the potato, then add the salt. Add the flour, then gradually mix in the water until you have a fairly tacky dough.

Turn the dough out on to a lightly floured work surface and knead for a few minutes until soft and pliable. Put it back in the bowl, cover it with a damp tea towel and leave it somewhere warm to rise for about an hour. When the dough has doubled in size, knock it back and turn it out on to the work surface again. Knead it into a loaf shape, tucking the edges under so you have a smooth, domed oblong. Put the dough in a loaf tin, cover again and leave to rise. Preheat the oven to its highest setting.

After about half an hour the bread should have risen well in its tin. Put it in the oven and immediately turn the temperature down to 220°C/Fan 200°C/Gas 7. Bake for about 30 minutes until the crust is firm and a deep golden brown and the base sounds hollow when you knock on it. Turn the loaf out on to a wire rack and leave to cool before using.

MIXED GRAIN BREAD FOR OPEN SANDWICHES

85 calories per thin slice

A slightly dense, filling loaf, this is good for slicing thinly and toasting or using as is for open sandwiches. It won't rise as much as an all-wheat loaf, but it is easy to make and tastes great. Using a starter mixture improves the taste and texture of the bread, but you do need to prepare that the day before.

Makes 1 loaf
Prep: 25 minutes, plus proving time
and starter fermentation
Cooking time: 30 minutes

Starter
100g strong white bread flour
125ml water
2g dried yeast (small pinch)

Dough
starter mix (see above)
150g white bread flour
100g wholemeal flour
150g rye flour
175ml water
5g dried yeast
1 tsp salt
1 tsp honey

oil, for spraying the tin

To make the starter mixture, put the ingredients in a bowl and mix them together – the mixture will be the consistency of a very sloppy dough or paste. Cover and leave at room temperature overnight or for at least 16 hours. You can leave the starter for a couple of days if you like, but your bread will taste much stronger.

To make the bread, put the starter into a large bowl (or the bowl of a food mixer) and add all the other ingredients. Mix until firm, then knead until you have a smooth dough. This will take at least 5 minutes with the dough hook on a food mixer, longer if kneading by hand. Then spend a couple of minutes stretching the dough away from you as far as possible and folding it back to you – this will help develop a chewy texture and introduce air bubbles into the dough.

Put the dough in a bowl and cover with a damp tea towel. Leave for at least an hour, preferably 2, until the dough is well risen. Lightly spray a 2lb loaf tin with oil.

Knock the dough back, shape it into a long oblong and put it into the tin. Cover again and leave for another 30–60 minutes. At this point, preheat the oven to its highest setting. If you put the bread on top of the oven, the residual heat will help with the proving.

When the dough has risen again and feels springy to the touch, put it in the oven. Immediately reduce the temperature to 220°C/Fan 200°C/Gas 7 and bake for about 30 minutes until a dark golden brown crust has formed and the bread sounds hollow when tapped on the bottom. Leave to cool on a wire rack.

Makes 4 portions of dip, 4 open sandwiches or 2 wraps

150g smoked trout fillets
2 tbsp low-fat crème fraiche
1 tsp horseradish sauce
¼ cucumber, peeled, deseeded and chopped
1 tbsp finely chopped dill
squeeze of lemon juice
flaked sea salt
freshly ground black pepper

Open sandwiches
2 cooked beetroot, thinly sliced
4 slices of firm bread, such as rye
a few sprigs of dill

Wraps
2 large tortilla wraps
bunch of watercress
2 cooked beetroot, finely sliced

SMOKED TROUT DIP OR FILLING

58 calories per portion (dip); 146 calories per open sandwich; 157 calories per wrap

Break the trout into small pieces, removing any bones, and put them in a bowl. In another bowl, mix the crème fraiche and horseradish. Add the cucumber and dill to the trout, then fold in the crème fraiche and horseradish mixture. Taste and season with salt and pepper and, if you think it needs it, a squeeze of lemon juice. If you are having this as a dip, purée or mash until it is quite smooth and serve with sticks of carrot, celery and cucumber.

To make open sandwiches, put a layer of beetroot on slices of bread and top with the trout. Garnish with a few sprigs of dill.

To make wraps, cover each tortilla wrap with sprigs of watercress, then follow with the beetroot. Pile the trout on top. Fold up the bottom of each wrap to stop everything falling out, then roll the whole thing up tightly. Cut in half on the diagonal. If you are not using immediately, wrap in foil or baking parchment for later.

Makes 4 portions of dip, 4 open sandwiches or 2 wraps

---

1 can of tuna in spring water
juice of 1 lime
2 tbsp light mayonnaise
1 tbsp low-fat crème fraiche
a dash of Tabasco
1 tbsp capers, chopped
¼ red pepper, finely chopped
2 spring onions, finely chopped
2 tbsp coriander, finely chopped

Open sandwiches
4 slices of bread
¼ cucumber
pinch of sugar
1 tsp white wine vinegar

Wraps
2 large wraps
2 large lettuce leaves, shredded
¼ cucumber, finely sliced lengthways
a handful of mint

TUNA AND CAPER DIP OR FILLING

61 calories per portion (dip); 118 calories per open sandwich; 236 calories per wrap

Drain the tuna and put it in a food processor with the lime juice, mayonnaise and crème fraiche and blitz until smooth. Stir in the rest of the ingredients and check for seasoning. Serve as a dip with sticks of carrot and cucumber or pile into lettuce leaves.

To make open sandwiches, slice the cucumber as thinly as you can. Dissolve a pinch of sugar in the vinegar and a tablespoon of water and pour this over the cucumber. Toss it lightly, then drain. Put the slices of cucumber on the bread and top with the tuna.

To make wraps, cover each wrap with lettuce, then follow with cucumber. Put the tuna mix on top, then add the mint. Fold up the bottom of each wrap to stop everything falling out, then roll the whole thing up tightly. Cut in half on the diagonal. If you are not using immediately, wrap in foil or baking parchment for later.

CARROT, RED PEPPER AND BUTTERBEAN DIP

64 calories per portion

You could use chickpeas or any other kind of bean for this but butterbeans do work well. There's very little oil in the dip, which saves on calories, but the crème fraiche or yoghurt really improves the texture and gives great mouth feel. Serve with some radishes and sticks of crunchy carrot, cucumber and celery.

Serves 8
Prep: 10 minutes
Cooking time: 35 minutes

2 large carrots, peeled and cut
   into rounds
1 head of garlic, broken into cloves
   and left unpeeled (2 cloves
   reserved)
1 large red pepper, deseeded
   and halved
1 tsp olive oil
400g can of butterbeans, drained
   and rinsed
1 tsp cumin
½ tsp sweet smoked paprika
¼ tsp cayenne or chilli powder
1 tsp tahini
2 tbsp low-fat crème fraiche
   or yoghurt
squeeze of lemon juice (optional)
flaked sea salt
freshly ground black pepper

To serve
1 tsp olive oil
extra paprika and cayenne

Preheat the oven to its highest temperature. Bring a saucepan of water to the boil and add the carrots and garlic – having set aside 2 of the cloves. Simmer for 15 minutes, then drain thoroughly and spread them over half of a roasting tin. Put the red pepper in the other half of the tin. Drizzle over the olive oil, then put the veg in the oven and roast for 20 minutes, until the carrots have started to take on colour and the red pepper is soft.

Put the red pepper in a bag or a covered bowl and set aside. When it is cool enough to handle, peel off the skin. Squeeze the flesh out of the garlic cloves and put this in a food processor with the red pepper, carrots, butterbeans, cumin, paprika, cayenne or chilli powder and the tahini. Finely chop the reserved garlic cloves and add those too. Season with salt and pepper.

Purée the dip until smooth, then fold in the crème fraiche. Taste for seasoning and add a squeeze of lemon juice if you like.

Scoop the dip into a bowl and serve drizzled with a teaspoon of oil and sprinkled with a little paprika and cayenne.

PAD THAI OMELETTE

359 calories per omelette

We love this recipe and it makes a perfect carb-free lunch. We've kept the calories down by using carrot, courgettes and bean sprouts instead of noodles. We do allow a sprinkling of peanuts, though, as they really make a difference to the flavour. If possible, use a large frying pan, about 23cm in diameter, so you can make very thin omelettes that roll up beautifully. And do check what tamarind paste you use. If it's concentrated, use just a teaspoon, but if not you'll need about a tablespoonful. Don't be tempted to add more, as it will upset the balance of flavours.

Serves 2
Prep: 20 minutes
Cooking time: about 15 minutes

1 tbsp vegetable oil
1 shallot, sliced
1 carrot, cut into matchsticks
1 small courgette, cut into matchsticks
5g chunk of fresh root ginger, peeled and finely chopped
1 red chilli, deseeded and sliced
2 garlic cloves, sliced
100g shelled raw tiger prawns, roughly chopped
100g bean sprouts
oil, for spraying
4 eggs
flaked sea salt
freshly ground black pepper

Sauce
1 tsp tamarind paste (1 tbsp if it's not concentrated)
1 tbsp fish sauce
1 tsp palm sugar (or caster sugar)
¼ tsp shrimp paste (optional)

To serve
2 spring onions, shredded
handful of coriander, chopped
1 tsp finely chopped peanuts

To make the sauce, mix all the ingredients together. Taste a little and adjust the quantities of any of the ingredients to taste.

To make the pad Thai, heat the oil in a wok until smoking, then add the shallot, carrot, courgette, ginger and chilli. Stir-fry for about 3 minutes until the vegetables are starting to cook through, then add the garlic. Stir-fry for another minute, then push everything to one side of the wok and add the prawns. Cook for another minute and then pour over the sauce. Let it bubble for a few moments and stir in the bean sprouts. Set it aside and keep warm.

Lightly spray a large non-stick frying pan with oil and place it over a medium heat until hot. Break 2 eggs into a bowl and whisk, then season with salt and pepper. Pour the eggs into the frying pan, swirling it around so the whole base is covered. Cook for a couple of minutes until the eggs are just about cooked through, then turn down the heat.

Put half of the pad Thai mixture in a line slightly to the side of the centre of the omelette. Sprinkle over half the spring onions, coriander and peanuts. Fold one side over the filling, then fold the other side over. Now roll the omelette over and out of the frying pan straight on to a plate. Repeat this with the other 2 eggs and the rest of the filling to make the second omelette and serve at once.

CRISPY CAULIFLOWER NUGGETS

130 calories per portion (if serving 4)

These crispy cheesy little morsels make a scrumptious starter or a snack to nibble on with a beer – and they are cheeringly low in calories. They're easy as anything to put together, but take care to drain the cauli carefully and watch that the breadcrumb mix doesn't get sticky or it will clump together and not coat properly.

Serves 4 as a starter or more
as a snack
Prep: 10 minutes
Cooking time: about 17 minutes

½ cauliflower, broken into small
    florets
6 tbsp low-fat natural yoghurt
75g very fine, dry breadcrumbs,
    such as Japanese panko
25g Parmesan cheese, finely grated
½ tsp paprika
1 tsp dried oregano or mixed herbs
oil, for spraying (optional)
flaked sea salt
freshly ground black pepper

Preheat the oven to 200°C/Fan 180°C/Gas 6. Line a baking tray with non-stick baking parchment.

Bring a large saucepan of water to the boil. Add some salt, then the cauliflower florets and blanch them for 2 minutes. Drain thoroughly and leave to dry in a colander until cool.

Put the yoghurt in a shallow bowl and mix the breadcrumbs, cheese, paprika and herbs in another bowl or plate.

Dip the cauliflower florets, a few at a time, into the yoghurt, then into the breadcrumb mixture. Toss them lightly until they are well coated with the breadcrumbs, then place them on the baking tray, spacing them out evenly. Give them a light spray of oil if you like, but this is not essential.

Bake the nuggets in the oven for 15 minutes until the coating is crunchy and starting to char slightly. Serve at once.

SWEET TREATS

More and more, we're realising that cutting down on sugar is just as important as keeping our fat intake under control, but like all our chums out there with a sweet tooth we don't need to despair. We've made our latest puds and bakes with as little sugar as possible, with the help of the natural sweetness in fruits such as berries, pineapple and bananas. We're particularly pleased with our fruity ice lollies, which give you a lovely sweet treat for less than 50 calories each.

SUMMER PUDDING

131 calories per portion (without crème fraiche)

There's virtually no fat in this traditional British dessert and if you use good ripe fruit you don't need much sugar either. A large white sandwich loaf works a treat for the bread casing.

Serves 6
Prep: 20 minutes, plus chilling time
Cooking time: 10 minutes

oil, for spraying
6 slices of white bread, crusts removed
300g strawberries, hulled and cut up if large
200g raspberries
200g blueberries
100g redcurrants, stalks removed, plus extra to garnish if you like
1–2 tbsp caster sugar

Lightly spray a 900ml pudding basin with oil, and line it with cling film. Take a slice of bread and cut it into a round that will fit into the bottom of the basin. Cut the rest of the slices into thirds, widthways and use most of these to line the sides. Overlap them very slightly with one another and the base to ensure there are no gaps and press the bread down as much as possible. You should have a couple of slices left over to put on top of the fruit.

Put all the fruit in a saucepan and sprinkle over a tablespoon of sugar. Add 3 tablespoons of water. Heat slowly, giving the sugar time to dissolve, then simmer very gently until the fruit is lightly cooked and has given out a lot of juice. The liquid should be a deep reddish purple. Stir as little as possible to avoid breaking up the fruit – you will find that most of the raspberries will break up anyway but that's fine, as they will provide juice for the pudding. Taste for sweetness and add more sugar, a teaspoon at a time and tasting after each addition, until you are happy with the flavour.

Ladle some of the fruit juice into the bottom of the basin and allow it to soak into the bread. Then with a slotted spoon, transfer all the fruit to the pudding basin. Pour in as much of the juice as possible, without it overflowing, then top with the remaining bread. Put a saucer on top of the pudding and weight it down with something heavy, such as a can of tomatoes. Put the pudding in the fridge and leave it for several hours, preferably overnight. Save any leftover juice for covering white patches and serving with the pudding.

When you are ready to serve, place a serving plate upside-down on top of the basin and turn the basin over to unmould the pudding. Carefully peel off the cling film. Cover any white patches with leftover fruit juice and garnish with extra berries if you have some. Serve with dollops of low-fat crème fraiche, if you like, but don't forget to add the extra calories.

RHUBARB AND ORANGE MERINGUE TARTLETS

153 calories per tartlet

Rhubarb can be tart and sour, but if your rhubarb is nice and pink and sweet you may get away with using even less sugar. This is a clever little pud.

Serves 6
Prep: 25 minutes
Cooking time: about 40 minutes

oil, for spraying
3 sheets of filo pastry

Filling
300g rhubarb, cut into 1cm rounds
2 tbsp caster sugar
zest and juice of 1 orange
1 tsp cornflour

Meringue
2 egg whites
100g sugar
1 tsp cornflour

Preheat the oven to 190°C/Fan 170°C/Gas 5. Lightly spray 6 holes in a muffin tray with oil.

To make the filo pastry cases, cut each sheet of filo into 8 squares. Layer 4 together, by overlapping them across one another so you end up with a multi-pointed star shape. Lightly spray the centre of each case with oil and bake them in the oven for 10 minutes, until they take on some colour.

To make the filling, put the rhubarb in a large saucepan and sprinkle over the sugar and orange zest. Add 50ml of water and cover. Cook very slowly over a gentle heat until the rhubarb is soft, then remove the rhubarb from the saucepan with a slotted spoon, leaving the juice in the pan.

Add the orange juice to the rhubarb juice in the pan. Mix the cornflour with a splash of water until it is smooth and add this to the saucepan. Heat slowly, while stirring, until the liquid thickens. Tip the rhubarb back into the saucepan and mix it with the sauce, being careful not to break up the rhubarb too much. Divide the filling between the 6 tartlet cases.

To make the meringue, whisk the egg whites until they have formed stiff peaks. Mix the sugar with the cornflour and gradually add this to the egg whites until you have a thick, glossy meringue. Pile the meringue on top of the rhubarb, forming peaks. The easiest way to do this is to spoon it on, but you can pipe it if you prefer.

Bake the tartlets in the oven for 15–20 minutes, until the meringue is golden brown, but still quite soft.

GINGER BISCUITS

58 calories per biscuit

We do like something to dunk and these are like little gingernuts, but they're quite chewy inside. The ground ginger makes them very gingery – for a milder biscuit, add just 1 teaspoonful.

Makes about 25
Prep: 10 minutes
Cooking time: 12–15 minutes

50g golden syrup
50g butter
100g light soft brown sugar
1 egg yolk
150g plain flour
½ tsp bicarbonate of soda
2 tsp ground ginger

Preheat the oven to 190°C/Fan 170°C/Gas 5. Line 2 baking trays with baking parchment.

Melt the golden syrup and butter together in a saucepan over a gentle heat. Remove from the heat and beat in the brown sugar and egg yolk.

Sift the plain flour, bicarb and ground ginger into a bowl. Add the wet ingredients and mix thoroughly. You might think the dough is too dry at first, as it will be very crumbly, but using your hands, keep working it together until it is smooth.

Roll teaspoons of the mixture (about 15g) into balls, then place them – spaced well apart, as they will spread – on the baking trays. Bake in the oven for 12–15 minutes until the biscuits are a rich golden brown and are cracked on the surface.

Remove the biscuits from the oven. They will be very soft, but don't worry, they will firm up very quickly. As soon as they are firm enough, transfer them to a cooling rack with a palette knife.

FREEZE!

The dough will freeze without any problem, and the biscuits can be frozen too. Just reheat them in the oven for a couple of minutes and then allow them to cool and crisp up again afterwards.

BANANA AND PINEAPPLE CAKE

205 calories per slice, if cut into 10; 171 calories per slice, if cut into 12

The banana and pineapple in this tantalisingly tropical cake keeps it lovely and moist and adds sweetness so you can keep the sugar content down. Just the thing with a cuppa to see you through to supper time.

Makes 1 cake with 10–12 slices
Prep: 20 minutes
Cooking time: 50–60 minutes

oil, for spraying
175g self-raising flour
2 tsp baking powder
½ tsp bicarbonate of soda
1 tsp grated nutmeg
75g soft light brown sugar
2 eggs
3 bananas (about 250g in weight), mashed
100g butter, melted
1 tsp vanilla extract
100g pineapple, finely diced

Preheat the oven to 180°C/Fan 160°C/Gas 4. Lightly spray the base and sides of a 2lb loaf tin with oil and line it with baking parchment.

Sift the flour, baking powder and bicarb into a large bowl and mix in the nutmeg and sugar. In a smaller bowl, beat the eggs, then add the mashed bananas, melted butter and vanilla extract. Add the egg mixture and the diced pineapple to the dry ingredients, then gently fold everything together until you have a pineapple-flecked batter.

Pour the batter into the prepared loaf tin and bake for 50–60 minutes, until a skewer comes out clean. Allow the cake to cool in the tin for 10 minutes, then transfer it to a cooling rack.

PLUM AND MAPLE SYRUP STEAMED PUDDINGS

234 calories per pudding

This makes 8 individual puddings – any leftovers can be frozen, either uncooked in the basin or cooked. Be careful not to overcook or the puddings could be dry. Lovely served with a little single cream or low-cal custard.

Makes 8 individual puddings
Prep: 20 minutes
Cooking time: 35 minutes

oil, for spraying
4 plums, stoned and diced
1 tbsp maple syrup
zest and juice of 1 orange
¼ tsp cinnamon

Sponge
175g self-raising flour
2 tsp baking powder
½ tsp cinnamon
pinch of salt
2 eggs
100g butter, melted and
  slightly cooled
100g maple syrup

Lightly spray 8 small pudding basins with oil. Preheat the oven to 190°C/Fan 170°C/Gas 5.

Put the plums in a small saucepan with the syrup, orange zest and juice and the cinnamon. Simmer over a medium heat until the plums have softened, but not broken down. Divide the plums and syrup between the pudding basins.

Sift the self-raising flour, baking powder and cinnamon into a large bowl, add a pinch of salt and stir well. In a separate bowl, beat the eggs, then add the butter and maple syrup. Pour the wet ingredients into the dry ingredients and mix thoroughly, then divide between the pudding basins.

Put the puddings in a roasting tin and pour in just-boiled water to come halfway up the sides of the basins. Bake in the preheated oven for 20–25 minutes.

Carefully remove the puddings from the hot water. Run a knife round the inside of each basin to release the pudding, then turn out on to serving plates. Great with single cream or low-cal custard.

WINE, ELDERFLOWER AND RASPBERRY JELLIES

153 calories per portion

Jellies for grown-ups, these are easy to prepare and they look and taste fab. We don't think it matters much if the fruit isn't evenly distributed, but we've given a few tips below if you want to try.

Pour the wine and cordial into a saucepan, add the sugar and heat until the sugar has dissolved. Put the sheets of gelatine in a bowl of cold water and leave them to soak until they've softened. Drain and wring out the gelatine, then add it to the wine mixture. Stir over a low heat until the gelatine has dissolved, but be careful not to let the mixture boil.

Strain the mixture into a jug. Divide the fruit between 4 glasses and pour over the wine mixture. Chill the jellies in the fridge until set – this should take 3–4 hours – or leave them overnight.

If you want an even distribution of the fruit you can stir the jelly every few minutes until it is almost set. Or, you can assemble the jellies in thirds: divide a third of the fruit between the glasses, top with the jelly mixture and allow to set in the fridge, then repeat the process twice more until you've used all the mixture.

Serves 4
Prep: 10 minutes, plus setting time

400ml white or sparkling wine
100ml elderflower cordial
1 tbsp caster sugar
5 sheets of leaf gelatine
200g raspberries

BAKED PEACHES

241 calories per portion without amaretto; 269 per portion with amaretto

Some peaches are sweet and delicious just as they are, but others need a little help and this recipe does the trick. The tiny bit of honey adds just enough sweetness. We don't think there's any need to skin the peaches and there's a danger of them collapsing if skinned.

Serves 4
Prep: 10 minutes
Cooking time: 25 minutes

4 peaches, cut in half and
    stones removed
4 tsp honey
2 tbsp chopped almonds
8 amaretti biscuits
25g butter, melted
8 tsp amaretto liqueur (optional)

Preheat the oven to 200°C/Fan 180°C/Gas 6. Put the peaches, cut side up, in an ovenproof dish or baking tray.

Drizzle a teaspoon of honey over each of the peach halves, then put them in the oven and bake for 10 minutes.

Put the almonds in a dry frying pan and cook them over a medium heat until very lightly toasted. Crush the amaretti biscuits until they resemble coarse breadcrumbs and mix them with the almonds. Pour over the butter and mix together.

Remove the peaches from the oven. Divide the nut and biscuit mixture between the peach halves and drizzle over the liqueur, if using. Bake for another 15 minutes until the peaches and topping are lightly brown. Spoon over any cooking juices and serve with low-fat crème fraiche if you like – but don't forget to add the extra calories to your total.

ICE LOLLIES

We made these in ice lolly trays with six holes, each holding about 50ml, but you can use any moulds you like – or even ice cube trays.

150ml reduced-fat coconut milk
150g fresh or canned pineapple
1 tbsp rum or Malibu
1 tbsp honey or sugar (optional)

PINA COLADA ICE LOLLIES

44 calories per 50ml lolly

Pineapples vary enormously in sweetness so you may or may not need to add honey to this.

Put the coconut milk, pineapple (drained, if using canned), and the rum or Malibu in a blender and blitz until smooth. Taste for sweetness and add some sugar or honey if you think it needs it, then blitz again. Spoon off any foam and pour the liquid into moulds or ice cube trays and freeze until set.

100ml fat-free natural yoghurt
1 banana (about 100g peeled weight)
juice of ½ lime
100g blueberries
a few drops of vanilla extract
1 tbsp honey

BLUEBERRY, BANANA AND YOGHURT ICE LOLLIES

45 calories per 50ml lolly

Put the yoghurt, banana, lime juice and half the blueberries in a blender with the vanilla and honey. Blend until fairly smooth – there'll probably still be some flecks of blueberry but that's fine. Add the remaining blueberries and pulse a couple of times to break them up roughly. Pour into moulds or ice cube trays and freeze until set.

200g strawberries
juice of 1–2 oranges (about 100ml)
juice of ½ lime
2 tbsp sugar

STRAWBERRY AND ORANGE ICE LOLLIES

35 calories per 50ml lolly

Put everything in a blender and blitz until smooth. If you want to get rid of the strawberry seeds, sieve the mixture before pouring it into your moulds or ice cube trays, then freeze until set.

MORE BREAKFAST AND BRUNCH

BIKER BREAKFAST MUFFINS

MASALA OMELETTE

MENEMEN (TURKISH EGGS)

FRENCH TOAST

SMOOTHIES

BREAKFAST CRANACHAN

STOVE-TOP GRANOLA

CAULIFLOWER RICE KEDGEREE

CORNED BEEF HASH

BIKER BREAKFAST MUFFINS

We reinvented the doner kebab and now it's the turn of the breakfast muffin – this is our guilty secret that isn't a secret any more. Okay, they're 500 calories but let's call them brunch and enjoy. The sausages lose a lot of fat when they're cooked in this way so that cuts the calories, or you could try making the chicken/turkey patties instead, which are definitely much lower cal. We love fried eggs and they're quicker than poached so extra good when you're in a rush.

Put a griddle pan over a high heat and leave it to get really hot – at least 5 minutes. If using sausages, remove the skins and shape each one into a very flat, round patty.

If you want to make the chicken or turkey patties instead of using sausages, put the mince in a bowl. Trim the bacon of fat and dice it as finely as you can, then add it to the bowl with the sage and the tomato purée. Season well with salt and lots of black pepper. Form the mixture into 4 patties.

When the griddle is too hot to hold your hand over, add whichever patties you've made. Grill them for 3 minutes on each side, adding a cheese slice, if using, to each for the last minute. If the griddle pan is hot enough, the patties will not stick.

Spray a large frying pan with low-cal oil. Break the eggs into the pan and cook them over a medium heat until the whites are just set.

Meanwhile, split and toast the muffins. Add a patty to 4 of the muffin halves. If you have time, trim the eggs for neatness and place an egg on top of each patty. Top with the remaining muffin halves and serve immediately. If you want to reduce the calorie count a little, leave off the top muffin.

SERVES 4

4 high-meat content sausages (about 65g each)

4 slices of reduced-fat cheese (optional)

low-cal oil spray

4 eggs

4 muffins

Chicken or turkey patties (optional)

250g lean turkey or chicken mince

1 rasher of smoked back bacon

1 tsp dried sage

1 tbsp tomato purée

flaked sea salt

freshly ground black pepper

500 calories per serving (fully loaded with cheese and muffin top and bottom)
444 calories per serving (as above, but with chicken or turkey patties)

MASALA OMELETTE

If you're the sort of person who often craves a curry, try this indulgent breakfast. It's a perfect example of our mantra – there are no calories in flavour. This is a great spicy kick-start of a dish and once you've got the spices out of the cupboard it's ready in no time.

SERVES 2

1 tsp coconut or vegetable oil

1 small onion, finely chopped

1 chilli, finely chopped

1 garlic clove, finely chopped

5g fresh root ginger, grated

½ tsp nigella seeds (optional)

1 tsp ground cumin

½ tsp ground turmeric

pinch of cinnamon

4 eggs, beaten

a few coriander leaves

flaked sea salt

freshly ground black pepper

190 calories per serving

Heat the oil in a large frying pan. Add the onion and cook it over a medium heat for about 5 minutes until it's just starting to colour. It's nice if the onion has a bit of bite to it so don't worry if it's not really soft.

Add the chilli (deseeded if you want), garlic, grated ginger and nigella seeds, if using. Sprinkle in the spices, then stir for a couple more minutes.

Season the eggs with salt and pepper. Pour the eggs into the frying pan and swirl the mixture around to make sure it covers the base of the pan evenly. Cook for a few minutes until the eggs are just set. Sprinkle with coriander leaves, roll the omelette up or cut it in half and divide it between 2 plates.

MENEMEN (TURKISH EGGS)

You get some fab breakfasts in Turkey and this is one of our favourites. It's so good you might find you like it better than a full English and the bonus is it's low in calories. We like to crumble in some feta when serving but it does add a few cals – up to you.

SERVES 4

1 tbsp olive oil

1 small red onion, finely chopped

1 red pepper, deseeded and diced

1 green pepper, finely diced

1 tsp hot smoked paprika or chilli powder

1 tsp dried oregano

1 tbsp tomato purée

4 medium tomatoes, diced or 200g canned chopped tomatoes

8 eggs, beaten

flaked sea salt

freshly ground black pepper

To serve

50g feta, crumbled (optional)

parsley or mint leaves, finely chopped

Heat the olive oil in a large frying pan that has a lid. Add the onion and peppers and cook them over a medium heat for about 10 minutes, covered, stirring regularly. They should still have some texture – you don't want them to be very soft.

Sprinkle over the paprika or chilli powder and the oregano. Add the tomato purée and cook for a further couple of minutes, then add the tomatoes and simmer for 5 minutes.

Season the eggs with salt and black pepper. Add them to the tomatoes and cook, stirring constantly, uncovered, until the eggs have completely combined with the tomato mixture and are just cooked through – the consistency should be soft. Serve immediately, sprinkled with feta, if using, and parsley or mint leaves.

Biker tip: If you're vegetarian, make sure the feta cheese you use is suitable and doesn't contain animal rennet.

V   *231 calories per serving*
264 calories per serving with feta

FRENCH TOAST

We both love French toast for a really indulgent breakfast treat – but it doesn't love our waistlines. So we've come up with a clever new version that cuts the fat right back and adds sweetness with a lovely apple compote. You could pop a few blackberries into the compote if you like or just scatter some on the plate. Lip-smackingly good.

First make the compote. Put the diced apples in a saucepan, squeeze the lemon juice over them and add 100ml of water. Simmer the apples over a low heat until they have softened and broken down – this only takes 5 minutes or so. Sprinkle in the cinnamon and pour over the maple syrup, then stir to combine. It's fine for the compote to be quite lumpy.

While the apples are cooking, get everything ready for the French toast. Break the eggs into a large bowl and add the milk, sugar and cinnamon. Whisk thoroughly until the eggs are completely broken up and combined with the other ingredients.

Heat a large frying pan and grease it with low-cal oil spray. Lightly wipe the pan over with kitchen towel to make sure the spray covers the base evenly. Press each slice of bread into the milk and egg mixture until it has just soaked through – don't let the bread become saturated or it will be in danger of falling apart. Shake off any excess and immediately drop the bread on to the frying pan and repeat with the other slices. Cook for a couple of minutes on each side until heated through and well browned on both sides.

Serve the French toast with the apple compote, a few blackberries, if you like, and a dollop of low-fat Greek yoghurt or crème fraiche.

SERVES 4

2 large eggs

200ml whole milk

1 tsp sugar

½ tsp cinnamon

low-cal oil spray

4 fairly thick slices of bread

Apple compote

2 large Bramley apples (about 300g peeled weight), peeled and diced

squeeze of lemon juice

½ tsp cinnamon

2 tbsp maple syrup

To serve

blackberries (optional)

low-fat Greek yoghurt or crème fraiche

281 calories per serving

SMOOTHIES

You can't say us Bikers don't move with the times – we're well up with smoothies. These make a proper get-up-and-go breakfast and you can take them to work with you if you like.

APPLE AND OAT SMOOTHIE

SERVES 2

2 eating apples, cored and roughly chopped

squeeze of lemon juice

2 tbsp porridge oats

200ml fat-free yoghurt

300ml semi-skimmed milk

½ tsp cinnamon

1 tsp honey

Put the chopped apples in a blender and squeeze the lemon juice over them. Add all the remaining ingredients and blitz until the mixture is as smooth as you can get it. Divide it between 2 glasses and serve at once.

275 calories per serving

AVOCADO, GRAPE AND SPINACH SMOOTHIE

SERVES 2

1 avocado

1 pear, roughly chopped

150g green grapes

handful of spinach

juice of 1 lime

handful of ice cubes

Peel the avocado and remove the stone. Put the avocado flesh in a blender with the rest of the ingredients and blitz until beautifully smooth. If the smoothie is too thick for your taste, add a little water to make the consistency you like. Divide between 2 glasses and serve at once.

244 calories per serving

BREAKFAST CRANACHAN

Breakfast doesn't get easier than this. Oats are a staple for us in the morning and this is a good twist on a bowl of porridge. Great for breakfast but can also be enjoyed of an evening with a tot of whisky if you want to treat yourself.

SERVES 4

40g porridge oats

200g raspberries and/or blueberries

400g low-fat or 0%-fat yoghurt

4 tsp honey

134 calories per serving

Put the porridge oats in a frying pan. Toast them over a high heat, stirring or shaking them regularly, until they smell nutty and have started to turn a light golden brown. Remove the pan from the heat, tip the oats on to a plate and leave them to cool for a couple of minutes.

Layer the berries, yoghurt and oats in individual glasses and drizzle a teaspoon of honey over each. Gently stir the mixture to get a nice ripple effect, then serve immediately before the oats go soft.

STOVE-TOP GRANOLA

When we first started dieting it was a real shock to find out that what we thought was a healthy granola breakfast actually had twice the calories of a fry-up. Best thing is to make your own granola and this version is cooked in a frying pan and takes minutes to put together. We think jumbo oats work best, as they give a chunkier texture.

SERVES 6

2 tbsp maple syrup

20g butter or coconut oil

150g jumbo oats

pinch of salt

1 tbsp sunflower seeds

2 tbsp flaked almonds

50g dried fruit

213 calories per serving (without milk or yoghurt)

Put the maple syrup and the butter or coconut oil in a large, preferably non-stick, frying pan and melt them together over a low heat.

Add the jumbo oats with a pinch of salt. Stir until the oats are completely coated with the melted syrup and butter, then turn up the heat to medium. Spread the oats evenly over the base of the pan, leave them for about 20 seconds, then stir and repeat. Keep doing this until all the oats have turned a golden brown and smell nutty – this will take about 5 minutes.

Add the sunflower seeds, nuts and fruit and stir for a couple of minutes longer. Tip the granola on to a plate and let it cool for 5 minutes – the oats will crisp up more. Serve at once with milk or yoghurt and store any leftovers in an airtight container for another day.

CAULIFLOWER RICE KEDGEREE

We're huge fans of cauli rice and cauliflower goes well with curry. Put them together and you've got kedgeree, which has always been a favourite of ours. Clever eh? This makes a cracking supper dish as well as a good way to start the day.

SERVES 4

4 eggs
500g cauliflower
500g smoked haddock, skinned
250ml whole milk
1 tsp coconut oil or vegetable oil
small bunch of spring onions, finely sliced into rounds
1 garlic clove, crushed
5g fresh root ginger, finely chopped
1 tbsp mild curry powder
150g frozen peas
small bunch of coriander (optional)

312 calories per serving

Boil a full kettle of water. Pour some just-boiled water into a small saucepan and bring it back to the boil. Add the eggs and boil them for 6 minutes. Remove the pan from the heat and run the eggs under cold water to cool them down.

While the eggs are cooking, divide the cauliflower into florets and put them, stalks and all, into a food processor. Blitz them to the texture of fine breadcrumbs.

Place the haddock in a shallow pan that has a lid and pour over the milk, then place the pan over a medium heat. Top up with just-boiled water from the kettle so the haddock is just covered, then bring the liquid back to the boil. Put a lid on the pan, remove it from the heat and leave it to stand for 10 minutes.

Melt the oil in a large frying pan over a gentle heat and add the spring onions. Cook them for a couple of minutes, then add the garlic, ginger and curry powder. Cook for a further minute.

Add the cauliflower to the frying pan and about 100ml of the haddock poaching liquid. Cook, stirring regularly, for about 5 minutes until the water has been absorbed and the cauliflower looks dry and fluffy.

Put the peas in the small saucepan and pour over some just-boiled water. Place the pan over the heat, bring the water back the boil and cook the peas for a couple of minutes. Drain and add the peas to the cauliflower.

Remove the haddock from its poaching liquid and break it up into small chunks, discarding any bones you may find. Peel the eggs and cut them into quarters.

Gently stir the haddock into the cauliflower rice, then top with the eggs and some coriander leaves if you like.

CORNED BEEF HASH

This is a proper feast of a breakfast and by using carrot and celeriac instead of potato, you cut calories and add flavour. We usually make this with a can of corned beef, which is good stuff, but we've also tried it with leftover home-made corned beef and it's even better. There's a recipe in our Meat Feasts *book if you want to try it. It's not as fatty as the tinned beef either.*

SERVES 4

200g celeriac, finely diced

200g carrots, finely diced

1 tsp dripping or fat scraped from the corned beef

1 onion, finely chopped

1 tbsp tomato purée

1 tsp Dijon mustard

200g can of corned beef or equivalent, diced

100ml beef stock

1 tsp Worcestershire sauce

low-cal oil spray

4 eggs

248 calories per serving

Bring a kettle of water to the boil while you prepare the celeriac and carrots. Put the veg in a saucepan and pour over just-boiled water to cover. Bring the water back to the boil, cover the pan and cook the vegetables for 7 minutes. They should be just cooked through. Drain thoroughly.

Meanwhile, heat the fat in a large frying pan. Add the onion and cook it over a medium heat until it's starting to soften. As soon as the vegetables are ready, add them to the frying pan along with the corned beef. Cook for 5 minutes until a crust has formed on the bottom of the mixture.

Put the tomato purée and mustard into a small bowl or jug with the beef stock and Worcestershire sauce and whisk well. Pour this mixture over the corned beef and vegetables and stir thoroughly. Cook for another 10 minutes, stirring every so often, until there are plenty of crusty brown bits interspersed through the mix.

While the hash finishes cooking, heat another frying pan and spray it with oil. Add the eggs and fry them until the whites have just set. Serve the hash with the eggs on top.

SOUPS AND STARTERS

PEA, LETTUCE AND ASPARAGUS SOUP

SPICY SWEETCORN SOUP

WILD MUSHROOM SOUP

CHILL-OUT SOUP

MEDITERRANEAN FISH SOUP

RED LENTIL AND BACON SOUP

BIKER CHICKEN SOUP

SPICY MUSSELS

AMERICAN-STYLE PRAWN COCKTAIL

SALT AND PEPPER SQUID

SALMON CEVICHE

PEA, LETTUCE AND ASPARAGUS SOUP

Get your fill of chlorophyll – this soup makes you feel healthy just looking at it. It's an ideal quick meal and the short cooking time keeps the lovely fresh green colour.

SERVES 4

10g butter
1 leek, trimmed and finely diced
100g thin asparagus spears
2 little gem lettuces, shredded
600g frozen peas or petits pois
1 litre hot vegetable stock
squeeze of lemon or lime juice
flaked sea salt
freshly ground black pepper

To serve
2 tbsp single cream
small bunch of basil or mint

220 calories per serving

Heat the butter in a large saucepan. Add the diced leek and a splash of water, then put a lid on the pan and leave it over a low heat for 5 minutes.

Cut the tips off the asparagus and set them aside for later. Finely slice the remaining stems and add these to the leeks, along with the shredded lettuce. Cook for another couple of minutes, then add the peas and pour the hot stock into the pan. Season with salt and pepper and leave the soup to simmer for 5 minutes.

While the soup is simmering, heat a griddle until it's very hot and grill the asparagus tips until they're nicely charred.

Blend the soup to a smooth texture. Taste, then squeeze in a little lemon or lime juice – just enough to bring out the flavour. If you have a mini blender or food processor, blitz the cream with the basil or mint, but if not, just finely chop the herbs and stir them into the cream.

Serve the soup drizzled with a little of the herb cream and topped with the grilled asparagus.

SPICY SWEETCORN SOUP

You know we like a bit of spice and heat, and this soup really does the trick. It's got a bacon garnish as well, but still comes in at only 274 calories a bowlful. Top that! Take a flaskful of this to work with you to keep your spirits up.

SERVES 4

2 tsp vegetable oil

1 small onion, finely chopped

1 red pepper, deseeded and diced

1 garlic clove, finely chopped

1 sweet potato, finely diced

3 tsp chipotle paste

1 tsp ground cumin

bunch of coriander, stems and leaves separated and chopped

700g frozen sweetcorn

400g can of chopped tomatoes

1 litre hot chicken or vegetable stock

75g smoked back bacon, trimmed of fat and cut into fine strips

flaked sea salt

freshly ground black pepper

274 calories per serving

Heat 1 teaspoon of the oil in a large saucepan. Add the onion and pepper and fry them gently for a few minutes, stirring regularly, then add the garlic and sweet potato. Stir for a minute.

Add 2 teaspoons of the chipotle paste and the cumin and stir to coat the vegetables. Add the chopped coriander stems and sweetcorn, then pour in the tomatoes and stock. Season with salt and pepper.

Bring the soup to the boil, then turn the heat down and simmer for 10 minutes, until the sweet potato is tender.

Meanwhile, heat the remaining oil in a small frying pan and fry the bacon for a couple of minutes. Add the rest of the chipotle paste and stir until the bacon is coated in the chipotle.

Ladle half the soup into a blender and blitz it to a purée, then tip it back into the saucepan with the rest. Alternatively, use a stick blender to whizz the soup so it thickens but still has some texture.

Serve in deep bowls garnished with the chipotle bacon and some coriander leaves.

Biker tip: For a vegetarian version, use veggie stock and garnish the soup with smoked tofu instead of bacon. Buy the firm tofu so you can crisp it up nicely before adding it to the soup.

WILD MUSHROOM SOUP

This is a beautifully rich and tasty soup with a proper mushroomy aroma. It's a soup for the gourmet and ideal for serving up to guests – no one will guess it's so low in calories. You don't have to use wild mushrooms; portobello, chestnut or button are fine, or try a mixture of them all. You could add a swirl of oil or crème fraiche to each serving if you're feeling fancy.

SERVES 4

20g dried wild or porcini mushrooms

150ml just-boiled water

10g butter

2 shallots or 1 leek, finely chopped

1 garlic clove, finely chopped

500g fresh mushrooms, wiped clean and sliced

700ml hot vegetable stock

a large sprig of thyme

25ml sherry or Marsala or juice of ½ lemon

2 tbsp finely chopped parsley

flaked sea salt

freshly ground black pepper

74 calories per serving

Put the dried mushrooms in a bowl. Pour the just-boiled water over them and leave them to soak for 10 minutes while you get on with the rest of the preparations.

Heat the butter in a heavy-based saucepan. Add the shallots or leek to the pan, put the lid on and leave to cook over a low heat for 5 minutes. Add the garlic and fresh mushrooms, turn up the heat and cook for a couple of minutes.

Strain the soaked mushrooms, reserving the liquid, then chop them finely and add them to the pan. Pour in the reserved liquid and the hot stock, then add the thyme and season with salt and pepper.

Bring the soup to the boil and simmer it for 5 minutes. Add the sherry, Marsala or lemon juice, remove the sprig of thyme, then blitz the soup in a blender. It should be a lovely rich brown. Serve immediately with a sprinkling of parsley.

MEDITERRANEAN FISH SOUP

This might look like a lot to do in half an hour, but it's really just a bit of chopping and then chucking it all in the pan. Very little cooking needed. The rouille is optional but really does add great flavour – rouille is the traditional accompaniment to Mediterranean fish soup and is served alongside for everyone to stir in as they like. It's usually made with shedloads of olive oil but our cheat's version is much lower in calories and still tastes the business.

If you're making the rouille, it's probably best to do this first and leave it to stand while you're preparing the soup. Put the saffron with a tablespoon of hot water in a small bowl. Add the mayonnaise and red peppers to a food processor with the lemon juice, then crush the garlic into this mixture and add the cayenne and the saffron water. Season with salt and pepper and blitz until smooth. Tip the rouille into a bowl, cover and set aside until needed.

Put the saffron for the soup in a small bowl with a tablespoon of hot water and leave it to steep while you prepare the vegetables.

Heat the olive oil and butter in a large saucepan or a casserole dish with a lid. Add the onion, garlic, leek and fennel and stir to coat them with the oil and butter, then add the whole chilli. Pour in the white wine and put the lid on the pan. Leave to cook gently over a low heat for 5 minutes.

Add the fish stock, orange peel, bay leaf and the saffron and its liquid. Season with salt and pepper, then bring the soup to the boil and leave it to simmer for a further 5 minutes. Add the courgette to the soup and cook for a further 3 minutes while you dice the fish.

Turn up the heat and add the fish and prawns, then the Ouzo or Pernod, if using. Put the lid on the pan and cook for 5–10 minutes or until the fish and prawns are cooked through. Sprinkle with parsley and serve with the rouille, if you've made some, on the side.

SERVES 4

pinch of saffron strands

1 tsp olive oil

5g butter

1 onion, finely chopped

3 garlic cloves, finely chopped

1 leek, trimmed and thinly sliced

1 fennel bulb, trimmed and thinly sliced

1 red chilli (optional)

100ml white wine

1 litre hot fish stock

1 strip of thinly pared orange peel

1 bay leaf

1 courgette, diced

500g white fish fillets, skinned

12 raw tiger prawns, peeled

1 tsp Ouzo or Pernod (optional)

2 tbsp finely chopped parsley

flaked sea salt

freshly ground black pepper

Rouille (optional)

small pinch of saffron

2 tbsp low-cal mayonnaise

2 roasted red peppers (from a jar)

juice of ½ lemon

1 garlic clove

pinch of cayenne

220 calories per serving

RED LENTIL AND BACON SOUP

This is a proper pick-me-up of a soup – comforting and rich in protein with the lentils. Red lentils cook quickly and break down nicely so you can make a good soup in a short time. Be sure to add hot stock though, or the cooking time will be longer. We like the chunky texture of this soup, but you can blend it if you like.

Heat the oil in a large saucepan and add the bacon, onion and red pepper. Cook over a low heat for 5 minutes, until the vegetables have started to soften.

Add the sweet potato, garlic and lentils to the pan and stir for a minute. Pour the hot stock into the pan, add the herbs and season with salt and pepper. Quickly bring the soup back to the boil over a high heat, then turn the heat down to medium and cover the pan. Cook for 15–20 minutes until the red lentils are tender. Take out the herbs before serving.

SERVES 4

1 tsp olive oil

75g smoked back bacon, trimmed of fat and diced

1 onion, finely chopped

1 red pepper, deseeded and diced

1.5 litres hot chicken or vegetable stock

1 small sweet potato, finely diced

1 garlic clove, finely chopped

200g red lentils

large sprig of thyme

1 bay leaf

flaked sea salt

freshly ground black pepper

321 calories per serving

BIKER CHICKEN SOUP

This is a meal in a bowl and even with a hunk of bread you come in at under 500 cals. It's what you bought that food flask for and is ideal for taking to work. We use cooked chicken breasts – available in every supermarket – for our quick version and it's a real feast. The tarragon is optional but it does add a lovely bit of extra flavour so pop some in if you can.

SERVES 4

1 onion, finely diced

1 large carrot, finely diced

1 celery stick, finely diced

150g butternut squash (peeled weight)

150g celeriac (peeled weight)

1 medium potato (about 150g), finely diced

2 leeks, cut into thin rounds

1 tbsp olive oil

50g smoked back bacon, trimmed of fat and diced

1 litre hot chicken stock

1 tsp dried oregano

1 bay leaf

1 sprig of tarragon (optional)

1 small green cabbage or a small bunch of kale or cavolo nero, finely shredded

2 cooked chicken breasts, finely shredded

small bunch of parsley, chopped

squeeze of lemon (optional)

flaked sea salt

freshly ground black pepper

Prepare the onion, carrot, celery, squash, celeriac, potato and leeks.

Heat the olive oil in a large saucepan, add the bacon and cook it over a high heat for a couple of minutes. Add the vegetables and cook them over a medium heat for 5 minutes, until they start to take on a little colour.

Pour the hot chicken stock into the pan and add the herbs, including the tarragon, if using. Season the soup with salt and pepper, bring it to the boil and then turn down the heat so it's cooking somewhere between a simmer and a proper rolling boil. Partially cover with a lid and leave for 5 minutes.

Meanwhile, prepare the cabbage, kale or cavolo nero and the chicken, add them to the pan and continue to cook for a further 10 minutes. By this point all the vegetables should be cooked through and the potato should have broken down a little.

Stir in most of the parsley, leaving a few leaves to garnish each serving. Taste and add a squeeze of lemon juice if you think the soup needs it.

363 calories per serving

SPICY MUSSELS

Mussels are cheap, tasty and nutritious. Eat more of them and you'll soon lose your belly and see your muscles! This spicy dish makes a good light meal on its own, perhaps with a bit of bread to mop up the delicious juices, but you can make it more substantial if you like by adding some canned cannellini beans. If you want to do this, add the beans with the passata and don't forget to tot up the calories too.

SERVES 4

1 tbsp olive oil

50g smoked back bacon, trimmed of fat and diced

1 onion, thinly sliced

2 garlic cloves, finely chopped

1 tsp fennel seeds

1 tsp hot paprika

grated zest of 1 lemon

100ml red wine

200ml tomato passata

1kg mussels

handful of parsley, finely chopped

flaked sea salt

freshly ground black pepper

160 calories per serving

Heat the olive oil in a heavy-based saucepan, then add the bacon and fry until it's crisp and brown. Remove it with a slotted spoon and set aside.

Add the onion to the pan and cook it gently for several minutes until it's starting to soften, then add the garlic, fennel seeds, paprika and lemon zest. Pour the red wine into the pan and let it bubble up for a minute or so, then add the passata. Turn the heat down to a simmer and put a lid on the pan. Leave for another 5 minutes.

While the sauce is simmering, clean the mussels under cold running water and pull off any beards. Tap any open shells and throw away any mussels that don't close tightly.

Add the mussels to the pan and put the lid back on. Cook for 3–4 minutes, shaking the pan regularly until the mussels have cooked through and have opened fully.

Sprinkle the bacon and parsley over the mussels. Check the seasoning and add salt and pepper if needed. Serve immediately, discarding any mussels that remain closed.

AMERICAN-STYLE PRAWN COCKTAIL

If you're in a big rush you can use ready-cooked prawns for this, but if you can spend a few minutes giving some raw prawns a spicy rub before whacking them on to a hot griddle you'll have something really special. Quick to do and so good to eat. The only problem is that it's so moreish you might be tempted to eat it all.

SERVES 4

20 raw large peeled prawns, tail tips attached if possible

1 tsp flaked sea salt

½ tsp white peppercorns

1 tsp garlic powder

grated zest of 1 lemon

1 tbsp olive oil

lemon wedges, to serve

Sauce

2 tbsp tomato ketchup

2 tbsp hot horseradish sauce

juice of 1 lemon

dash of Tabasco sauce

dash of Worcestershire sauce

pinch of paprika (optional)

flaked sea salt

freshly ground black pepper

Heat a griddle pan for a few minutes until it's very hot. Check the prawns and remove the black line running down the back – this is the intestinal tract. Put the prawns in a bowl.

Grind the salt, peppercorns, garlic powder and lemon zest together with a pestle and mortar, then stir in the olive oil. Add the mixture to the bowl with the prawns and rub it into them, making sure they are all well coated.

Cook the prawns on the hot griddle for a minute or so on each side until they're pink and just cooked through.

For the sauce, mix together all the ingredients (except the paprika and seasoning) in a small bowl. Season with salt and pepper and sprinkle with a little paprika if you like. Serve the prawns with the sauce for dipping, with extra lemon wedges for squeezing over the top.

103 calories per serving

SALT AND PEPPER SQUID

Deep-fried squid is good but so is this griddled version – and it's far lower in calories. You can buy cleaned squid at fish counters so all you need to do is open out the tubes and score them as we describe below. If the tentacles are included, cook them too. Enjoy with a dash of Tabasco.

Place a griddle pan over a high heat for at least 5 minutes, while you get the squid ready.

Take each squid pouch or tube and pull off the fins if they're still attached. Slide your knife inside the top opening of the pouch, then cut down the side, so you can open the squid out into a flat piece. Lie the piece outer side down and lightly cut a diagonal pattern over the inner side with a sharp knife, making sure that you don't cut right the way through. Do the same with the fins. Cut the tubes into strips 2cm wide.

Crush the black peppercorns, mix them with the sea salt and lemon zest and sprinkle the mixture over the squid – tentacles too, if you have them. Drizzle over the olive oil.

Cook the squid on the hot griddle for 1–2 minutes on each side until nicely charred – the pieces of squid will curl round on themselves, which is fine. You may have to cook the squid in a couple of batches so you don't overcrowd the griddle. If so, make sure the griddle is still very hot when you start the second batch.

Serve the squid piping hot, with a squeeze of lemon juice and a dash of Tabasco, if you like. Or if you want some extra zing, sprinkle the squid with Szechuan peppercorns – half a teaspoon should do it.

SERVES 4

500g small squid, cleaned

1 tsp black peppercorns

1 tsp crushed sea salt

grated zest of 1 lemon

1 tbsp olive oil

To serve

lemon wedges

Tabasco sauce (optional)

½ tsp Szechuan peppercorns

121 calories per serving

SALMON CEVICHE

Ceviche is a Peruvian favourite – it's really just thinly sliced raw fish served in citrus juices and other flavourings. The marinade 'cooks' the fish so it has a lovely texture but still tastes really fresh. This makes a perfect starter or a light lunch.

SERVES 4

400g salmon fillet

2 spring onions

4 radishes

1 tbsp finely shredded coriander leaves

1 tbsp finely shredded basil leaves

Dressing

juice of 2 limes

juice of 1 orange

1 garlic clove, finely chopped

5g fresh root ginger, finely chopped

1 red chilli, finely chopped

1 tbsp finely chopped coriander stems

flaked sea salt

freshly ground black pepper

First make the dressing. Mix the lime and orange juice in a bowl and add the garlic, ginger, red chilli and coriander stems. Season with salt and pepper, then leave the dressing to stand for 5 minutes while you prepare the fish and vegetables.

Using a sharp, long-bladed knife, carefully slice the salmon as thinly as you can. Start with the knife just under the surface and cut very thin slices on the diagonal towards the tip of the fillet, as you would for smoked salmon. Discard the skin. Arrange the slices on 4 plates.

Cut each spring onion in half, lengthways, then shred finely. Cut the radishes into thin slices and sprinkle them over the salmon.

Finally, drizzle the dressing over the salmon – it should be well covered – then sprinkle with shredded coriander and basil leaves. Serve immediately.

229 calories per serving

SALADS AND SAVOURY SNACKS

HARISSA VEGETABLES AND JUMBO COUSCOUS

SEVEN-LAYER SALAD

SUMMERY GREEN COLESLAW

COURGETTE AND CHICKPEA SALAD

GREEN PASTA

SMOKED TROUT SALAD

QUINOA, PRAWN AND MANGO SALAD

BANG-BANG CHICKEN SALAD

LENTIL AND MERGUEZ SAUSAGE SALAD

LUNCH BOX POT NOODLES

BREAD TARTLETS

CINEMA SNACKS

HARISSA VEGETABLES AND JUMBO COUSCOUS

Jumbo couscous was new to us but it's a wonderful thing – it gives a salad good body and texture. We like this salad by itself for lunch or with some grilled chicken for supper. If you like, you can make this even lower in calories by replacing the couscous with blitzed cauliflower.

Heat the oil in a large frying pan. Add the onions and red peppers and fry them over a high heat for 5 minutes. Add the courgettes, then continue to cook for another couple of minutes.

Add the lemon zest and cumin seeds. Whisk the tomato purée with the harissa paste and the 100ml of stock or water, then pour this over the vegetables and cover the pan. Turn the heat down and simmer for another 5 minutes until the vegetables are softened but still with a bit of bite to them.

While the vegetables are cooking, pour the 500ml of stock or water into a pan, add the couscous and season it with salt and pepper. Bring it to the boil, cover the pan and simmer for 6–8 minutes until the couscous has plumped up and is tender. Remove the pan from the heat and drain off any remaining liquid.

Add the tomatoes to the frying pan with the vegetables and leave them to soften, covered, for a further minute.

Mix the couscous with the salad leaves, then add the vegetables and their dressing. Squeeze over a little lemon juice and sprinkle liberally with the mint and parsley leaves.

SERVES 4

1 tsp olive oil

2 red onions, finely sliced into wedges

2 red peppers, deseeded and cut into strips

2 large courgettes, cut thinly on the diagonal

zest of 1 lemon

1 tsp cumin seeds

1 tbsp tomato purée

1 tbsp harissa paste

100ml hot vegetable stock or water

12 cherry tomatoes, halved

Couscous and salad

500ml vegetable stock

100g jumbo couscous

200g salad leaves

squeeze of lemon juice

handful of mint leaves

handful of parsley leaves

flaked sea salt

freshly ground black pepper

197 calories per serving

SEVEN-LAYER SALAD

This is a pick-and-mix of joy and a feast for your eyes and for your ever-reducing belly. Looks like loads of ingredients we know but there's nothing complicated – just chopping, mixing and assembling. The trad way of serving this is in layers in a big glass bowl but we like to arrange the layers in stripes on a platter.

If using frozen sweetcorn, cook it in boiling water for a couple of minutes, then drain and cool. Shred the lettuce heart, drain and rinse the black beans, and coarsely grate the Cheddar.

To make the tomato salsa, mix the tomatoes, red peppers, red onion and coriander stems in a bowl and sprinkle over the cumin. Season with salt and pepper and add the lime juice. Stir thoroughly.

To make the chicken salad, put the chicken and celery in a bowl. Mix the buttermilk with the mayonnaise and whisk in the white wine vinegar and lime juice. Season with salt and pepper, then stir the buttermilk mixture into the chicken and celery.

For the avocado salad, peel and stone the avocado, then cut the flesh into thin slices. Grate the courgette and finely chop the spring onions. Put them in a bowl, season with salt and pepper and squeeze over the lime juice. Fold together gently so you don't break up the avocado too much.

If you're serving the salad in a glass bowl, put the lettuce in the base, then add the remaining layers – sweetcorn, black beans, tomato salsa, chicken salad, avocado and grated cheese. Put them in whatever order you like, but the grated cheese should be on the top. To serve, mix with salad servers after everyone has seen and admired the layers.

For serving on a platter, arrange the layers in stripes – again, in whatever order you like. No need to mix – just let everyone help themselves.

SERVES 4

200g sweetcorn, canned or frozen

1 romaine lettuce heart

400g can of black beans

25g Cheddar or other hard cheese

Tomato salsa

3 tomatoes, finely chopped

2 roasted red peppers (from a jar), finely chopped

½ small red onion, finely chopped

2 tbsp coriander stems, finely chopped

1 tsp cumin

juice of 1 lime

sea salt

freshly ground black pepper

Chicken salad

3 cooked chicken breasts, skinned and diced

1 celery stick, finely chopped

2 tbsp buttermilk

2 tbsp low-cal mayonnaise

1 tsp white wine or cider vinegar

squeeze of lime juice

Avocado salad

1 avocado

1 courgette

2 spring onions

juice of 1 lime

446 calories per serving

SUMMERY GREEN COLESLAW

Fresh, crunchy and full of flavour, this green coleslaw really smacks of summer. Nice with lots of herbs but add them just before serving, as they start to go black and limp after being torn and chopped. Good with a turkey burger.

SERVES 4

100g frozen peas or baby broad beans, cooked and cooled

1 small green cabbage, shredded

1 large courgette, grated or sliced into matchsticks

1 large fennel bulb, trimmed and sliced into matchsticks

1 bunch of spring onions, finely sliced

2 celery sticks, finely chopped

1 green apple, grated

juice of ½ lime

bunch of basil leaves, torn

bunch of mint leaves, chopped

flaked sea salt

freshly ground black pepper

Dressing

2 tbsp low-fat yoghurt

2 tbsp low-fat mayonnaise

zest and juice of 1 lemon

1 tbsp finely chopped tarragon

pinch of sugar

Bring a pan of water to the boil, add the peas or beans and bring the water back to the boil. Cook for 2 minutes, then drain.

Put the cabbage, courgette, fennel, spring onions and celery in a large bowl and add the cooked peas or broad beans. Mix the grated apple with the lime juice, then add it to the vegetables. Season with salt and pepper, then stir well to combine.

Whisk together all the dressing ingredients and season with salt and pepper. Pour the dressing over the vegetables. Garnish with the basil and mint leaves just before serving.

V   *130 calories per serving*

COURGETTE AND CHICKPEA SALAD

The chickpeas make this a good hearty salad. We like adding broad beans, but if you don't have any it'll still taste good. Or you could add a few green peas instead. The dressing is really tangy and tasty so take the time to make it – trust us, it's worth it. We love the cinnamon which adds a lovely warm hit of Middle Eastern flavour – Morocco comes to Morecambe.

SERVES 4

2 courgettes, trimmed

low-cal oil spray

100g frozen broad beans

1 tbsp olive oil

2 garlic cloves, finely chopped

zest and juice of 1 lemon

1 tsp cumin

pinch of cayenne

pinch of cinnamon

100g rocket leaves

400g can of chickpeas, drained and rinsed

small bunch of mint, chopped

small bunch of basil, torn

flaked sea salt

freshly ground black pepper

143 calories per serving

Preheat your grill until it's really hot. Meanwhile, cut the courgettes into thin diagonal slices. Spray a baking tray with oil, then arrange the slices of courgette on it and season them with salt and pepper. Grill the courgette slices for 3–4 minutes on each side until nicely browned around the edges.

While the courgettes are grilling, bring a kettle of water to the boil, pour some of the water into a saucepan and bring it back to the boil. Add the broad beans, cook them for about 3 minutes, then drain.

Heat the olive oil in a small frying pan, add the chopped garlic and fry it very briefly making sure it doesn't take on any colour. Add the lemon zest and juice and the spices. Season with salt and pepper. Swirl the pan around a little to combine everything, then remove it from the heat and set aside.

Wash the rocket leaves and put them in a salad bowl. Add the chickpeas to the bowl along with the grilled courgettes and broad beans. Pour the garlicky dressing over the salad and toss, then add the chopped mint and basil leaves. Serve immediately.

Biker tip: If you want to freeze this salad, freeze it without the rocket leaves and herbs. Add them after defrosting.

GREEN PASTA

Pasta and pesto is one of our favourite suppers, but the regular version contains lots of oil, cheese and nuts so is quite rich. Try our healthier, lighter recipe, which cuts down the calories but not the flavour and uses a little of the pasta cooking water to thicken the sauce – classic Italian tip. Eat this warm, or cool as a salad. Makes a great lunch box salad too.

Bring a full kettle of water to the boil, then pour the water into a large saucepan. Put a lid on the pan and bring the water back to the boil, then add plenty of salt and the pasta. Cook the pasta for 10–12 minutes, or until cooked through but still with a bit of bite to it, adding the grated courgette at the last minute.

Put the basil, garlic, oil and lemon zest in a food processor with a small ladleful of the cooking liquor – do this towards the end of the cooking time so the water will have more starch in it. Season with salt and pepper. Blitz the sauce until it's fairly smooth but still flecked with green from the basil.

Drain the pasta and courgette, toss it with the sauce and serve with grated Parmesan cheese.

SERVES 4

200g short pasta

1 large courgette, grated

1 large bunch of basil

1 garlic clove, finely chopped

1 tbsp olive oil

grated zest of 1 lemon

25g Parmesan cheese or a vegetarian alternative, grated

flaked sea salt

freshly ground black pepper

---

239 calories per serving

SMOKED TROUT SALAD

Fillets of smoked trout make a quick, easy and nourishing salad and the celeriac fries add a crispy crunch. Get those going right away so they can be cooking while your prepare the rest of the salad and you'll be sitting down to a tasty feast in no time. You need hot-smoked trout (or salmon) for this, as it flakes nicely. Thinly sliced fish doesn't work.

SERVES 4

200g celeriac, peeled weight

low-cal oil spray

100g green beans

100g salad leaves, such as spinach, baby kale, pea shoots or lamb's lettuce

250g cooked beetroot, cut into wedges

200g smoked trout

small bunch of dill, leaves only

a few chives

flaked sea salt

freshly ground black pepper

Dressing

75ml buttermilk or low-fat yoghurt

1 tsp cider vinegar

2 tsp Dijon mustard

½ tsp runny honey

135 calories per serving

Preheat the oven to 220°C/Fan 200°C/Gas 7. Cut the celeriac into very fine matchsticks. The easiest way to do this is to cut it into thin slices first, using a mandolin if you have one, and then into fine strips. Spritz a baking tray with low-cal oil and spread the celeriac strips over it. Sprinkle them quite generously with salt, and pepper, then spray with oil again.

Bake the celeriac fries in the oven for 20 minutes, turning them over every 5 minutes or so, until they have shrunk down and cooked through. You will find some strips are well browned and crunchy while others are slightly softer, but the contrast is good. The fries will crisp up further as they cool.

While the celeriac is cooking, prepare the rest of the salad. Trim the green beans and cut them in half. Cook them in a saucepan of boiling water for 4–5 minutes or until tender, then drain.

Spread the salad leaves over a large platter and add the beans, beetroot and celeriac fries.

Break up the trout into chunks and add these to the salad. Separate the dill into small fronds and snip the chives with scissors, then sprinkle them over the salad.

Whisk the salad dressing ingredients together and season with salt and pepper. Drizzle the dressing over the salad and serve.

QUINOA, PRAWN AND MANGO SALAD

Bold, zesty flavours make this a real treat and you wouldn't believe how well the mango and prawns go together. Do your best to allow time to marinate the prawns briefly, as it really does make a difference. The time it takes for the griddle to heat up is long enough. If you fancy, you could add some thinly sliced courgettes or some briefly cooked green beans to this.

SERVES 4

100g quinoa

200ml hot vegetable or chicken stock or water

1 tsp olive oil

grated zest of 1 lime

2 garlic cloves, crushed

400g raw king prawns, shelled

1 mango

1 red chilli, deseeded and roughly chopped

5g fresh root ginger, roughly chopped

1 tsp white wine vinegar

juice of 1 lime

200g salad leaves, such as rocket, baby spinach or lamb's lettuce

4 spring onions, cut into 2cm diagonal slices

small bunch of coriander, leaves only

a few basil leaves

flaked sea salt

freshly ground black pepper

200 calories per serving

Rinse the quinoa thoroughly under running water, then drain it well. Put the quinoa in a saucepan and cook it over a medium heat for a minute to help develop a nutty flavour, then pour over the stock or water. Season with salt and pepper. Bring the liquid to the boil, then cover the pan and turn the heat down to a simmer. Cook for 15 minutes, then remove the pan from the heat and leave the quinoa to stand for 5 minutes. Remove the lid and leave to cool for a few minutes.

Meanwhile, get on with the rest of the salad. Place a griddle on the hob to heat up. Put the olive oil in a bowl with the lime zest and add the crushed garlic. Add the prawns and season them with salt and pepper, then leave them to marinate and absorb the flavours for 5 minutes. By then, the griddle should be good and hot so cook the prawns for a minute or so on each side until they are pink. Set them aside.

Peel the mango. Cut half the flesh into strips or cubes for the salad and set them aside. Put the rest of the flesh into a blender or food processor, squeezing the big seed between your hands to get any further juice. Add the chilli and ginger to the blender, together with the white wine vinegar and lime juice, then season with salt and pepper. Blitz until smooth to make the dressing.

To serve, arrange the salad leaves on a large platter and sprinkle the quinoa on top. Add the spring onions and half the herbs, then top with the reserved mango and griddled prawns. Drizzle over the mango and chilli dressing, sprinkle with the rest of the herbs and serve immediately.

BANG-BANG CHICKEN SALAD

This really is banging – a good substantial chicken salad that everyone is going to love. And you'll have most of the stuff for the sauce in your cupboard. To make this even quicker, use leftover chicken or bought chicken breasts and just shred them into the peanut sauce. Super tasty and more bangs for your buck.

Cut the chicken into thin slices and put them in a bowl. Sprinkle over the Chinese five-spice powder and rub it into the chicken.

Add the oil to a wok and place it over the heat. When the oil in the wok is shimmering, add the chicken and fry it briskly for 2–3 minutes until it is cooked through. Pour over the soy sauce and cook for a further minute. Remove the chicken from the wok and put it on a plate to cool down a little.

Now make the peanut sauce. Heat the vegetable oil in the wok and add the shallot or onion, garlic and ginger. Stir-fry for a couple of minutes over a very high heat, then add all the remaining sauce ingredients. Simmer until the sauce is slightly syrupy and well combined, then leave to cool while you make the salad.

Arrange the cabbage, carrot, courgette, bean sprouts and spring onions on a large platter. Add the chicken, then drizzle over the peanut sauce. Sprinkle with the chillies and some coriander leaves.

SERVES 4

400g skinless chicken breasts

1 tsp Chinese five-spice powder

1 tsp vegetable oil

1 tbsp soy sauce

Peanut sauce

1 tsp vegetable oil

1 shallot or small onion, finely chopped

2 garlic cloves, finely chopped

10g fresh root ginger, grated

1 tsp hot sauce

200ml hot chicken stock

1 tbsp lime juice

1 tbsp soy sauce

1 tsp runny honey

1 tbsp crunchy peanut butter

a few drops of sesame oil

Salad

1 large Chinese cabbage, shredded

1 carrot, cut into matchsticks

1 courgette, cut into matchsticks

50g bean sprouts

bunch of spring onions, shredded

2 red chillies, deseeded and finely sliced

small bunch of coriander, leaves only

208 calories per serving

LENTIL AND MERGUEZ SAUSAGE SALAD

Lentils and sausages always work well together and this salad is no exception – it's particularly good served warm. The dressing is fab and there's no oil so it's nice and low cal.

SERVES 4

1 small red onion, sliced into crescents

pinch of sea salt

6 merguez sausages, sliced fairly thinly on the diagonal

200g baby spinach, well washed

250g cooked green or puy lentils (from a can or pack)

1 red pepper, deseeded and diced

2 tbsp finely chopped parsley

Dressing

200g cherry tomatoes, cut into quarters

1 tsp mustard

2 tsp red wine vinegar

pinch of sugar

flaked sea salt

freshly ground black pepper

Heat a griddle pan for at least 5 minutes until it's extremely hot. Put the onion in a small bowl, sprinkle it with salt and pour over some cold water. Leave it to stand for 5 minutes, then drain.

Grill the sausages on the hot griddle for a couple of minutes on each side, until cooked through and well charred. Remove them from the heat and set aside.

Divide the spinach between 4 plates. Arrange the lentils, red pepper and drained red onion over the spinach, then top with the cooked sliced sausages.

For the dressing, put the tomatoes in a frying pan and warm them through until they start giving out juice. Whisk the mustard, red wine vinegar and sugar into the juices and cook for a further minute or so. Season with salt and pepper.

Drizzle the tomato dressing over the salad and sausages, then sprinkle with parsley and serve immediately.

Biker tip: If you want to freeze this salad, freeze it without the rocket leaves and herbs and add them after defrosting.

319 calories per serving

LUNCH BOX POT NOODLES

Take this to the office for your lunch and your workmates will look on in envy. We've suggested three different seasonings and you'll probably come up with your own variations too – let us know! It's really important to use the right kind of noodles – you want the sort that will cook in two or three minutes. Vary the veggies as you like but choose things that cook in about the same time as the noodles. No need to defrost the peas, as they will defrost when you add the hot water.

SERVES 2

2 small nests of quick-cook noodles

1 small carrot

1 small courgette

½ red pepper

2 spring onions

4 mushrooms

1 garlic clove, finely chopped

5g fresh root ginger, finely chopped

2 tbsp frozen peas

50g cooked chicken

small bunch of fresh coriander

flaked sea salt

freshly ground black pepper

Thai seasoning

1 chicken stock cube, crumbled

1 tbsp Thai green curry paste

1 tbsp fish sauce

juice of 1 lime

Miso seasoning

1 tbsp instant miso

a few thin strips of nori seaweed

1 tbsp tamari or soy sauce

Chinese seasoning

1 tsp Chinese five-spice powder

1 chicken stock cube, crumbled

1 tbsp soy sauce

Divide the noodles between 2 large, lidded, heatproof jars.

Grate the carrot and cut the courgette and red pepper into thin matchsticks. Thinly slice the spring onions and the mushrooms. Layer the vegetables on top of the noodles, then sprinkle over the garlic and ginger, followed by the peas. Finely dice or shred the chicken and add this too, then top with some coriander leaves.

Add the ingredients for your choice of seasoning – Thai, miso or Chinese – and a little salt and black pepper. Seal with the lid. When you are ready to cook your pot noodles, pour over freshly boiled hot water. Leave the lid sitting on top and leave for 4–5 minutes, prodding regularly with a fork or a chopstick so the seasonings mix and dissolve into the water.

When the noodles have softened, continue to mix, then eat while still hot. Season with some extra soy, fish sauce and lime juice if you like.

322 calories per serving

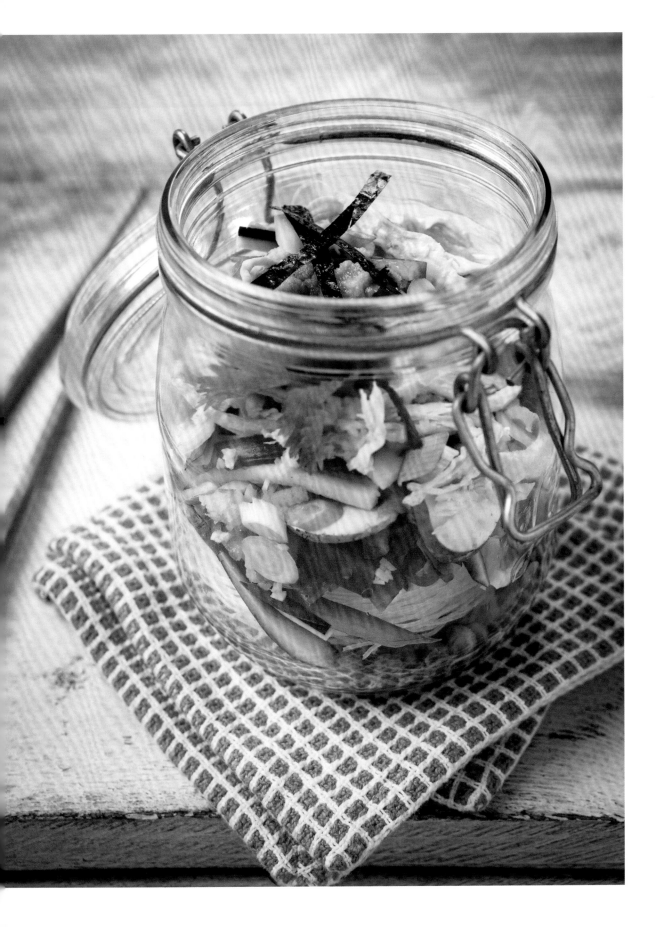

BREAD TARTLETS

These mini-quiches for dieters make a cracking savoury snack – and we've come up with a cheeky sweet version too! Once you cut rounds out of the slices of bread you will have quite a lot of trimmings. We don't like waste so we leave them to dry out, blitz them to breadcrumbs and stash them in the freezer to use another time.

MAKES 8

low-cal oil spray

8 slices of white sandwich bread or thick sliced bread

75g half-fat crème fraiche

1 egg

1–2 tsp Dijon mustard

40g cooked ham, diced

1 tbsp finely chopped parsley

20g Cheddar cheese, grated (optional)

flaked sea salt

freshly ground black pepper

❄ *134 calories per tartlet*

Preheat the oven to 220°C/Fan 200°C/Gas 7. Spray a fairy cake tin with oil. Cut the crusts off the slices of bread and roll each slice flat with a rolling pin. Cut out rounds using a 7.5–8cm pastry cutter.

Press the rounds into the fairy cake moulds – when firmly in the corners the sides should still reach the top of the tin. Spray the bread cases with oil again, then bake them for 7–8 minutes until crisp but with very little colour.

Meanwhile, whisk the crème fraiche and egg together until smooth and season with salt and pepper.

When the tartlet cases have finished baking, remove them from the oven, leaving the oven on. Dollop a small amount of mustard in the centre of each tartlet and spread it over the base. Add a little ham, then spoon in some of the crème fraiche and egg mixture, filling the tarts right to the top. Sprinkle with parsley and grated cheese, if using. Put the tartlets back in the oven and bake for about 10 minutes until just set.

Biker tip: We couldn't resist trying a sweet version of these. Make the cases as above. While they're baking, mix 60g of half-fat crème fraiche with 1 egg and a tablespoon of maple syrup. Fill the tartlets and top with a grating of nutmeg, then bake as above – 133 calories each.

CINEMA SNACKS

BAKED TORTILLA CHIPS

4 corn tortillas

sea salt

25g Cheddar cheese or a vegetarian
alternative, grated (optional)

Spice mix (optional)

1 tsp cumin

1 tsp chilli powder

1 tsp garlic or onion granules

zest of 1 lime

1 tsp salt

Salsa

3 medium red tomatoes

1 small red onion

2 tbsp chopped coriander leaves

juice of 1 lime

½ tsp cumin

1 tsp chipotle paste or hot sauce

Preheat the oven to 200°C/Fan 180°C/Gas 6. Cut each of the tortillas into 3 pieces horizontally so you have 2 half moons and 1 rectangle. Cut each half moon into 3 triangles, then the rectangle into 6 triangles.

Arrange the pieces on a couple of baking trays and sprinkle them with salt. If you are using the cheese, sprinkle it over the tortilla chips. For the spice mix, combine the spices and garlic with the lime zest and a teaspoon of salt and sprinkle this over the chips.

Bake the chips for 8–10 minutes until golden brown in places and crisp and dry. They will continue to crisp up as they cool down.

While the chips are in the oven, make the salsa. Finely chop the tomatoes and onion and put them in a bowl with the coriander and lime juice. Stir in the cumin and chipotle paste or hot sauce and season with salt if needed. Serve with the chips.

V *170 calories per serving (with salsa)*

SPICED POPCORN

1 tsp vegetable oil

75g popping corn

1 tsp mild chilli powder

zest of 1 lime

1 tsp salt

1 tbsp lime juice

Heat the oil in a large lidded saucepan. Add the popping corn and put the lid on the pan. Cook over a medium heat for about 4–5 minutes, shaking regularly when the corn starts popping, and holding down the lid.

When the popping has stopped completely (when you go for about 15 seconds without hearing any sound), it will be safe to remove the lid. Tip the popcorn into a bowl, discarding any kernels that haven't popped.

Mix the chilli powder, lime zest and salt together. Shake this mixture over the popcorn, making sure it is all well dusted, then sprinkle over the lime juice.

V *81 calories per serving*

FULLER FASTER

SPICY SWEETCORN FRITTERS

HAM AND PEA FRITTERS

GRILLED AUBERGINES WITH CHICKPEA AND SPINACH SALAD

WHITE BEAN AND TUNA FISHCAKES

MARINATED FISH WITH STIR-FRIED GREENS

BAKED FISH WITH GREEN AND WHITE BEANS

FISH VÉRONIQUE

CHILLI PRAWN PASTA

GRILLED CHICKEN WITH FENNEL SAUCE

SZECHUAN CHICKEN STIR-FRY

CHICKEN LIVERS – ESCABECHE STYLE

PORK MEDALLIONS IN BBQ SAUCE

LAMB STEAKS WITH MINT AND BROAD BEANS

STEAK WITH CHEAT'S 'BÉARNAISE'

SPICY SWEETCORN FRITTERS

You're going to love our Hairy Biker fitter fritters! These little numbers are good served with salad or slices of ham and also make a nice starter with this tangy dipping sauce.

MAKES 12

300g frozen sweetcorn

3 eggs

1 tbsp soy sauce

1 tsp sriracha hot sauce or similar

60g plain flour

1 tbsp finely chopped coriander stems

1 garlic clove, finely chopped

1 spring onion, finely chopped

low-cal oil spray

flaked sea salt

freshly ground black pepper

Dipping sauce

2 tbsp soy sauce

juice of 1 lime

½ tsp sugar or honey

1 tsp red chilli flakes

1 garlic clove, finely chopped

Bring a kettle of water to the boil. Put the sweetcorn in a heatproof bowl, pour over some boiling water and leave for a minute or so while the sweetcorn defrosts. Drain and set aside.

Crack the eggs into a separate bowl and beat them until well broken up. Add the soy sauce and hot sauce and season with salt and pepper. Sprinkle over the plain flour and whisk to combine, making sure there are no lumps. Add the coriander stems, garlic, spring onion and sweetcorn to the batter and stir thoroughly.

Heat a large frying pan and spray with oil, covering the base as evenly as possible. Dollop heaped tablespoons of the batter on to the pan, spacing them out well. You should be able to cook 4 or 5 fritters at once, but don't be tempted to crowd the pan or it will be hard to turn them. Cook the fritters for 2–3 minutes until well browned underneath, then flip them and cook on the other side. Remove the fritters from the pan and set them aside to keep warm while you cook the rest.

While the fritters are cooking, make the dipping sauce. Put the soy sauce and lime juice in a small bowl, add the sugar or honey and stir until completely dissolved. Add the chilli flakes and garlic, then leave to stand until ready to serve.

V ❄ *57 calories per fritter*

HAM AND PEA FRITTERS

It's the peas that give these fritters their amazing colour and they are superb, we promise you. Like the sweetcorn fritters, these are good on their own with a little sauce or served up with some veg, salad or whatever you fancy.

MAKES 12

300g frozen peas
60g plain flour
1 tsp baking powder
2 eggs
2 tbsp milk
100g cooked ham, diced
low-cal oil spray
flaked sea salt
freshly ground black pepper

Mustard sauce
1 tsp ready-made mustard
4 tbsp 0% fat natural yoghurt

69 calories per fritter

Put the peas in a sieve and run hot water over them to defrost. Bring a kettle of water to the boil, then pour some into a small saucepan. Add the peas, bring the water back to the boil and cook for 2 minutes. Drain the peas, then purée them roughly – you want a mixture of whole and crushed peas. You can do this in a food processor or simply mash the peas in a bowl.

Put the plain flour in a large bowl with the baking powder and season with salt and pepper. Make a well in the flour and break in the eggs. Break up the eggs with a fork and start working in the flour from the sides of the bowl until it is all mixed in. Add the milk and whisk to make a smooth batter. Stir in the peas and ham.

Heat a large, shallow non-stick frying pan and spray the base with oil. Add tablespoons of the batter, spacing them out well. You should be able to cook 4 or 5 at a time but don't overcrowd the pan. Cook the fritters for 2–3 minutes until they are well browned underneath, then flip them and cook them on the other side. Remove the fritters from the pan and set them aside to keep warm while you cook the rest.

Stir the mustard into the yoghurt to make the sauce and serve with the fritters.

GRILLED AUBERGINES WITH CHICKPEA AND SPINACH SALAD

The aubergines make a great starter just with the yoghurt sauce but they're even better with the chickpea salad too. This is a good vegetarian dish, but check the feta you're using is suitable and not made with animal rennet.

Put the grill on to heat up to its highest setting while you prepare the aubergines. Top and tail the aubergines, making sure you cut at least 1cm away from the top, as this can be a bit tough. Cut the aubergines into ½cm slices. You should get at least 12 good-sized slices from each aubergine, as well as the smaller end bits.

Spritz 2 non-stick baking trays with low-cal oil spray and arrange the aubergine slices on the trays. Spray the aubergines with oil and season them with salt and pepper. Place one of the trays under the grill, preferably on the second shelf down (they will burn if right at the top), then grill the slices for 5 minutes. Turn them over and grill for another 5 minutes or 3 minutes if adding feta.

If using feta, crumble half of it over the grilled aubergine slices, then grill for a further 2 minutes. Remove the tray from the grill, then cook the second batch in the same way.

While the aubergines are grilling, make the yoghurt dressing. Soak the saffron in the hot water for 5 minutes. Whisk the saffron and its soaking liquor into the yoghurt with the garlic and dried mint. Season with salt and pepper and serve with the aubergine slices and the chickpea and spinach salad.

Chickpea and spinach salad

Heat the oil in a large saucepan and add the garlic. Cook it for a minute, then add the chickpeas, cumin, lemon zest and 50ml of water. Season with salt and pepper and leave to simmer over a low heat until warmed through.

Thoroughly wash the spinach and shake it briefly to get rid of any excess water. Add the spinach to the pan, pushing it down as it wilts. Leave it for a couple of minutes to combine with the chickpeas, then stir.

SERVES 4

3 medium aubergines

low-cal oil spray

50g feta cheese (optional)

flaked sea salt

freshly ground black pepper

Yoghurt dressing

large pinch of saffron

30ml hot water

200g low-fat or 0% fat Greek yoghurt

1 garlic clove, crushed

1 tsp dried mint

Chickpea and spinach salad

1 tsp olive oil

1 garlic clove, finely chopped

400g can of chickpeas, drained and rinsed

1 tsp ground cumin

grated zest of 1 lemon

200g fresh baby leaf spinach

205 calories per serving

WHITE BEAN AND TUNA FISHCAKES

Everyone loves a fishcake, and tuna and white beans are a classic combo. You can use any kind of canned fish for these – salmon, sardines, mackerel – as long as it's packed in spring water, as this reduces the calories by a lot. BTW, you might be tempted to throw everything into the food processor at once, but don't. We've tried doing this different ways and it really is worth blitzing the beans and the fish separately to get the right texture – otherwise the beans get too smooth and claggy. And you don't need to wash the food processor in between so it doesn't take much longer.

Preheat the oven to 220°C/Fan 200°C/Gas 7. Put the beans in a food processor and pulse a few times until they have broken down a little but are not completely puréed. You want a fairly coarse but uniform texture. Tip the beans into a large bowl.

Put the fish in the food processor with the onion and parsley and blitz until everything is well combined and the parsley is very finely chopped. Add this mixture to the bowl with the beans.

Add the mustard, egg, lemon zest and juice to the beans and fish, and season generously with salt and pepper. Mix thoroughly, then taste again for seasoning.

Sprinkle the panko breadcrumbs over a plate. Shape the fish and bean mixture into 8 patties, dip them in the breadcrumbs, then pat off any excess. Spritz a non-stick baking tray with low-cal oil spray and place the fishcakes on it. Spray the top of the fishcakes with oil.

Bake the fishcakes in the oven for about 15 minutes, turning them halfway through the cooking time.

While the fishcakes are baking, make the sauce. Simply mix all the ingredients in a bowl and stir well, then season with salt and black pepper.

MAKES 8 FISHCAKES

2 x 400g cans of cannellini beans, drained and rinsed

2 cans of fish in spring water, drained weight 200–250g

1 onion, very finely chopped

small bunch of parsley, roughly chopped

2 tsp Dijon mustard

1 egg, beaten

grated zest and juice of 1 lemon

100g panko breadcrumbs

low-cal oil spray

flaked sea salt

freshly ground black pepper

Sauce (optional)

grated zest and juice of 1 lemon

1 tbsp finely chopped capers

1 tbsp finely chopped cornichons

1 tbsp Dijon mustard

150ml 0%-fat yoghurt

175 calories per fishcake

MARINATED FISH WITH STIR-FRIED GREENS

We love our fish and this excellent dish has become a firm favourite of ours. We did want to make it a one-pot but instead it's a two-pot wonder. Just works better if the fish and veggies are cooked separately. And don't forget – that extra bit of washing-up burns calories.

SERVES 4

juice of 1 orange

3 tbsp soy sauce

1 tsp runny honey

10g fresh root ginger

2 garlic cloves

4 x 150g skinless salmon fillets

2 tsp vegetable oil

low-cal oil spray

1 tsp sesame oil

2 tsp sesame seeds

flaked sea salt

freshly ground black pepper

Stir-fried greens

2 tsp vegetable oil

6 spring onions, cut into rounds

1 green pepper, finely diced

1 red chilli, finely diced

1 green pointed cabbage or similar, cut into quarters and shredded

441 calories per serving

Put the orange juice in a bowl with the soy sauce and honey. Grate the ginger and crush the garlic into the bowl. Whisk thoroughly to combine and dissolve the honey, then season with salt and pepper.

Put the salmon in the bowl and coat it with the marinade. Leave to stand for a few minutes.

Heat the vegetable oil in a wok. When the oil in the wok starts to shimmer, add all the stir-fry ingredients and cook them for 2–3 minutes. Turn down the heat slightly.

While the vegetables are cooking, remove the salmon fillets from the bowl and put them on some kitchen paper to drain. Reserve the marinade. Spray a frying pan with low-cal oil and place it over a medium heat. Put the salmon fillets in the frying pan and cook them for 2–3 minutes on one side, then turn them over.

Add a tablespoon of the marinade to the vegetables in the wok and allow them to simmer for a few minutes. Pour the remaining marinade around the salmon – it should reduce to a thin syrup while the salmon is cooking. Flip the salmon over one more time just to get a coating of the reduced marinade.

Drizzle the sesame oil over the vegetables and divide them between 4 plates. Add the salmon and drizzle over any remaining marinade. Sprinkle with sesame seeds and serve immediately.

BAKED FISH WITH GREEN AND WHITE BEANS

This is a lovely comforting supper dish and it's very easy to put together. It works best with a nice thick piece of white fish.

SERVES 4

4 x 150g white fish fillets (cod or haddock)

200g green beans, trimmed and halved

1 tbsp olive oil

1 small red onion, finely sliced into crescents

2 garlic cloves, finely chopped

grated zest of 1 lemon

100g cherry tomatoes, halved

2 x 400g cans of cannellini beans, drained and rinsed

bunch of basil, leaves torn

flaked sea salt

freshly ground black pepper

315 calories per serving

Preheat the oven to 200°C/Fan 180°C/Gas 6. Line a baking tray with baking parchment, put the fish fillets on the tray and season them with salt and pepper.

Bring a kettle of water to the boil. Pour the water into a saucepan and bring it back to the boil. Add the green beans and cook them for 3–4 minutes until they're just done. Drain the beans and set them aside.

While the beans are cooking, start on the sauce. Heat the olive oil in a large saucepan while you prepare the onion and garlic. Add the onion to the pan and cook it gently over a medium heat for a few minutes – you want it to colour a little but still have some bite. Then add the garlic and lemon zest and cook for another minute.

Put the fish in the oven and bake it for 12–15 minutes.

While the fish is cooking, finish the sauce. Add the tomatoes to the saucepan with the onion and garlic, along with the cannellini beans and the green beans. Season with salt and pepper. Cook gently for a few minutes until the tomatoes have just warmed through and have started to release some of their juices.

When the fish is cooked serve it with the beans, liberally sprinkled with torn basil leaves.

Biker tip: If you do have a bit longer than half an hour, you could brine the fish before baking. It only takes 20 minutes and it firms the fish up nicely. Mix one part of salt with 9 parts of water in a bowl. Add the fish and leave for 20 minutes, then drain well.

FISH VÉRONIQUE

We're very happy that we can enjoy this dieter's version of a French classic and we think you will be too. It's traditionally made with Dover sole, but that's expensive so we use lemon sole instead. Other options are tilapia, plaice or any other white fish that keeps its shape and doesn't flake away to nothing. Ask the people at your fish counter to skin the fillets for you.

SERVES 4

5g butter

1 shallot, very finely chopped

100ml vermouth or white wine

250ml hot fish stock

2 large sprigs of tarragon, plus 2 tbsp finely chopped tarragon leaves

200g white grapes

100ml single cream

600g thin white fish fillets, skinned

flaked sea salt

white pepper

231 calories per serving

Melt the butter in a large frying pan that has a lid. Add the shallot and cook it over a low heat for 5 minutes until it's starting to soften. Pour the vermouth or white wine into the pan and let it boil for a minute, then add the fish stock along with the sprigs of tarragon. Bring the liquid back to the boil and cook it quite vigorously for 5 minutes until it's reduced by about a third.

Cut the grapes in half, add them to the pan and simmer them for a couple of minutes, then pour in the single cream. Season with salt and white pepper, add the finely chopped tarragon leaves and stir to combine. Continue to simmer the sauce for a couple of minutes until it has a consistency slightly thicker than single cream.

Cut the fish fillets in half lengthways, then slice each diagonally across the middle.

Carefully arrange the pieces of fish over the sauce. Put the lid on the pan and simmer for another 3–4 minutes, until the fish has just cooked. Serve immediately.

CHILLI PRAWN PASTA

With chilli, garlic and lime, this pasta dish is brimming with bold flavours and makes a proper filling dinner. If you do happen to have some vodka handy, we recommend adding a dash. It works a bit of extra magic.

SERVES 4

200g spaghetti

1 small onion, finely chopped

1 red pepper, deseeded and finely chopped

2 garlic cloves, finely chopped

1 tbsp olive oil

1 tsp chilli flakes

grated zest of 1 lime

100ml hot fish or vegetable stock

250ml tomato passata

50ml vodka (optional)

400g shelled raw prawns (defrosted if frozen)

small bunch of coriander or basil

lime wedges, for serving

flaked sea salt

freshly ground black pepper

341 calories per serving

Start by putting a full kettle of water on to boil. Pour the boiled water into a large saucepan, put a lid on the pan and bring the water back to the boil. Season with plenty of salt, then add the spaghetti. Cook for 10–12 minutes until the pasta is tender but still has a little bite to it, then drain.

Meanwhile, prepare the onion, pepper and garlic. Heat the olive oil in a large lidded frying pan, then add the onion and red pepper along with a splash of water. Cover the pan and cook over a medium heat until the veg are starting to soften. Add the garlic, chilli flakes and lime zest, then season with salt and pepper. Pour the stock into the pan, put the lid back on and cook the sauce for another 5 minutes.

Pour in the passata and simmer for a further 5 minutes. Add the vodka, if using, then simmer for a minute or so more. Throw in the prawns and cook until they have just turned pink and opaque – they should still be quite bouncy.

Serve the sauce with the pasta and a sprinkling of coriander or basil leaves to garnish. Add some lime wedges for everyone to squeeze over their helping.

GRILLED CHICKEN WITH FENNEL SAUCE

We use butterflied chicken breasts here – that means breasts that are cut halfway through the middle and opened out so they are nice and thin and cook quickly. This isn't hard to do, but if you ask at your butcher's shop or meat counter they might prepare them for you. If you don't have a large enough griddle to cook all the chicken breasts at once, do them in batches, starting before you cook the fennel.

First prepare the chicken. Place a breast on the work surface, with the top side (the side that would have had the skin attached to it) facing up. Put one hand on top of the chicken breast and take a sharp knife in your other hand. Slice into one side of the breast and keep on slicing through horizontally until you are nearly, but not quite, through to the other side. Now open up the chicken and press the centre flat – it will look like a cross between a butterfly and a love heart. Repeat with the remaining breasts.

Put the chicken breasts in a bowl and season them well with salt. Whisk the oil and lemon juice together and pour them over the chicken. Using your hands, rub the mixture into the chicken, then set the bowl aside. Wash your hands thoroughly.

For the sauce, trim the fennel, reserving any fronds for a garnish, and dice it quite finely. Melt the butter in a small pan and add the fennel. Cook it over a high heat for a couple of minutes, then turn the heat down, cover the pan and leave the fennel to braise gently for 8–10 minutes until it's translucent and almost tender.

While the fennel is braising, finely dice the tomatoes. Put a griddle pan to heat up for several minutes.

Turn up the heat under the pan of fennel and add the vermouth or white wine. Boil until it's reduced down by half, then add the lemon zest and tomatoes. Season with salt and pepper, then leave to simmer for 5 minutes. Tear the basil leaves and stir them into the sauce, then remove the pan from the heat.

Arrange the opened-out chicken breasts on a griddle. Cook them for 3–4 minutes on each side until they have charred lines across their surface and are cooked through. Serve the chicken with the sauce, garnished with a few fennel fronds saved from the bulb.

SERVES 4

4 skinless chicken breasts

1 tsp olive oil

juice of ½ lemon

flaked sea salt

freshly ground black pepper

Fennel sauce

1 large fennel bulb

10g butter

2 large tomatoes, finely diced

50ml vermouth or white wine

grated zest of 1 lemon

a few basil leaves

220 calories per serving

SZECHUAN CHICKEN STIR-FRY

At only 200 calories per serving, you can afford to have a bit of rice alongside this spicy stir-fry. But not too much — rice is what makes Sumo wrestlers fat.

First prepare the chicken. Slice the meat into thin strips, trimming off any visible fat. Cut the woody ends off the asparagus, then slice the stems into lengths of about 5cm. Finely chop the garlic cloves and ginger, then cut the spring onions into thin rounds. Lightly crush the Szechuan and black peppercorns together.

Whisk together all the sauce ingredients until the honey has dissolved.

Heat the vegetable oil in a wok until smoking. Add the strips of chicken and cook them for 3 minutes, stirring constantly, then add the asparagus and baby corn. Continue to cook for a further 2 minutes, then add the garlic, ginger and spring onions. After another minute, add the crushed peppercorns and cayenne or chilli, if using.

Pour the sauce over the chicken and cook for a few minutes more until everything is cooked through and the sauce has reduced a little. Garnish with a few coriander leaves and sesame seeds, if using. Serve with noodles or rice if you like, but don't forget to add the extra calories to your total.

SERVES 4

500g skinless chicken breast or thigh fillets

200g asparagus spears

2 garlic cloves

5g fresh root ginger

4 spring onions

1 tsp Szechuan peppercorns

1 tsp black peppercorns

2 tsp vegetable oil

200g baby corn

½ tsp cayenne or red chilli pepper (optional)

Sauce

2 tbsp soy sauce

1 tbsp rice wine vinegar

1 tsp runny honey

100ml chicken stock

1 tsp sesame oil

Garnish

coriander leaves

1 tsp white or black sesame seeds (optional)

200 calories per serving

CHICKEN LIVERS – ESCABECHE STYLE

Chicken livers are cheap, nourishing and cook really fast. What's more they're full of flavour and we think they should be used more than they are. Escabeche is kind of like a warm pickle and is popular in Latin America. This dish encapsulates those sweet, savoury and sour escabeche flavours that we love in a healthy way. Trust us -- it's good.

Heat a teaspoon of the olive oil in a large lidded frying pan and add the onions and red peppers. Cook them over a high heat for a couple of minutes, then add a splash of water, cover the pan and turn down the heat. Leave to cook for 5 minutes.

Add the garlic and cook for a further minute, then remove the onions, peppers and garlic from the pan and set them aside. Add the remaining olive oil to the pan and turn the heat up high. Add the chicken livers and cook them for 2 minutes on each side, then put the onions, peppers and garlic back in the pan.

Whisk the sherry vinegar, Tabasco, honey, tomato purée and chicken stock together in a small bowl and pour the mixture over the chicken livers. Leave to simmer for a few minutes to make sure the livers are cooked through and the vegetables have softened nicely. Sprinkle with plenty of oregano or parsley leaves and serve.

SERVES 4

2 tsp olive oil

2 red onions, sliced into thin wedges

2 red peppers, deseeded and sliced

2 garlic cloves, finely chopped

400g chicken livers, trimmed

1 tbsp sherry or red wine vinegar

dash of Tabasco sauce

½ tsp runny honey

1 tbsp tomato purée

100ml chicken stock

fresh oregano or parsley

167 calories per serving

PORK MEDALLIONS IN BBQ SAUCE

Kids love this – we love this – and it makes a dead tasty supper. Some green veg is good alongside the pork and maybe some sweet potato mash – it echoes the sweetness of the pork nicely. Or the sweetcorn fritters (see page 260) would work well too. Be sure to have the pan really good and hot for searing the meat and a word of caution – don't cook the medallions for too long or they could be dry.

SERVES 4

1 pork tenderloin (about 600g), trimmed of fat

2 tsp vegetable oil

flaked sea salt

freshly ground black pepper

BBQ sauce

½ onion, roughly chopped

3 garlic cloves, roughly chopped

1 tbsp red wine vinegar

1 tbsp tomato purée

1 tbsp Worcestershire sauce

1 tbsp dark soy sauce

juice of 1 orange

250ml chicken stock

1 tbsp maple syrup (optional)

½ tsp hot sauce (optional)

239 calories per serving

Cut the tenderloin into 1½–2cm slices – you should get about 16 pieces. Season the meat with salt and pepper, then set it aside for a few minutes.

For the sauce, put the onion and garlic in a blender or food processor with the red wine vinegar, tomato purée, Worcestershire sauce and soy sauce. Season with salt and pepper, then blitz until you have a smooth sauce. Tip this into a small saucepan and add the orange juice, stock, maple syrup and the hot sauce, if using.

Bring the mixture to the boil and allow it to bubble quite fiercely for 10 minutes or until it has reduced by a half to a third and is thick and syrupy. Keep stirring the sauce regularly to make sure it doesn't catch on the bottom of the pan. Turn down the heat and leave the sauce to simmer while you start cooking the pork.

Heat the vegetable oil in a large frying pan. Add the pork slices and sear them on each side for a minute. You'll probably need to do this in batches so you don't overcrowd the pan. When all the slices are seared, put them back into the pan. Pour over the sauce and leave the pork to simmer for at least 5 minutes, until it's cooked through and has added flavour to the sauce.

LAMB STEAKS WITH MINT AND BROAD BEANS

We've suggested marinating the lamb steaks briefly for extra flavour here. Yes, marinating and cooking all in half an hour seems a tall order, but it can be done and is well worth it. The broad beans are a perfect accompaniment. We always have some broad beans in the freezer and this method of stewing them with tomatoes and spices turns them into something special.

SERVES 4

4 lamb steaks, about 150g each

2 tsp olive oil

1 tbsp red wine vinegar

2 tsp dried mint

½ tsp sugar, runny honey or pomegranate molasses

1 tsp cumin (optional)

Broad beans

500g frozen broad beans

2 tsp olive oil

1 onion, finely chopped

2 garlic cloves, finely chopped

grated zest of ½ lemon

1 tsp cumin

pinch of cinnamon

1 tsp dried oregano

200ml hot chicken stock or water

200g canned tomatoes

juice of ½ lemon

1 tsp pomegranate molasses (optional)

small bunch of parsley, finely chopped

flaked sea salt

freshly ground black pepper

406 calories per serving

First marinate the lamb. Trim the lamb of any fat. Whisk the olive oil and red wine vinegar in a bowl with the mint, sugar, honey or pomegranate molasses and the cumin, if using. Rub the mixture into the lamb steaks and leave them for at least 10 minutes, preferably a little longer. (If you have the chance to do this in advance, so much the better.)

While the lamb is marinating, get on with the beans. Put the broad beans in a heatproof bowl, pour some boiling water over them and leave for a minute or so while the beans defrost. Drain and set aside.

Heat the olive oil in a saucepan and add the onion. Cook gently over a medium heat for a few minutes, then add the garlic, lemon zest, spices and oregano. Season with salt and pepper, then add the broad beans and the stock or water. Bring to the boil, then turn down the heat, cover the pan with a lid and cook for 5 minutes.

At this point, put a griddle pan on the hob to heat up – it will need at least 5 minutes.

Add the tomatoes, lemon juice and pomegranate molasses to the broad beans and leave to simmer gently while you cook the lamb.

Shake off any excess marinade from the lamb steaks, then place them on the griddle. Cook for 2–3 minutes on each side until well charred on the outside but still pink in the middle. Remove from the griddle and allow them to rest for a few minutes.

Serve the lamb steaks with the broad beans, garnished with finely chopped parsley.

STEAK WITH CHEAT'S 'BÉARNAISE'

We couldn't do a book on fast food without a steak recipe – the ultimate fast but delicious supper. These steaks are served with our cheat's version of the classic steak sauce – Béarnaise.

SERVES 2

2 thin sirloin steaks, about 150g each, trimmed of fat

Sauce

1 small shallot, finely chopped

small bunch of tarragon, roughly chopped

50ml white wine or vermouth

1 tbsp white wine vinegar

100ml half-fat crème fraiche

2 egg yolks

½ tsp Dijon mustard

a few chives

squeeze of lemon juice

flaked sea salt

white pepper

Tomato and onion salad

2 medium tomatoes, thinly sliced into rounds

½ small red onion, finely chopped

1 tsp olive oil

a few tarragon leaves and chives, finely chopped

First, take your steaks out of the fridge so they can come up to room temperature before you cook them. If you've just got home with them, better still. Just leave them on one side while you start the sauce.

Put the shallot and tarragon in a small saucepan. Add the wine or vermouth and the vinegar, bring to the boil, then boil for a minute. Leave to stand for a few minutes.

Put the griddle pan on the hob so it can start heating up. Season the steaks with salt.

Now make the salad. Prepare the tomatoes and onion and arrange them on a serving plate. Drizzle them with the olive oil, season with salt and pepper and sprinkle with the herbs. Set the salad aside until ready to serve.

To finish the sauce, strain it through a fine sieve and discard the solids, then pour the liquid back into the small saucepan. Add the crème fraiche to the pan and season with salt and white pepper. Heat the sauce until it has loosened, then whisk in the egg yolks and mustard. Add the tarragon mixture, the chives and a squeeze of lemon juice, then whisk very briskly until the sauce becomes frothy. Keep it warm and give it another quick whisk before serving.

Put the steaks on the hot griddle. For medium-rare meat, cook them for 2 minutes on the first side and 1½ minutes on the second; for rare, 1½ minutes on the first side, then 1 minute on the second; for medium, cook the steaks for 2 minutes on each side.

Remove the steaks from the griddle and leave them to rest for 5 minutes before serving with the sauce and the salad.

QUICK FEASTS

THAI VEGETABLE CURRY

BLACK-EYED PEAS AND GREENS

FISH CURRY

FISH CRUMBLE

CHICKEN AND PRAWN LAKSA

TURKEY KEEMA PEAS

STICKY CHICKEN DRUMSTICKS

CAULIFLOWER PILAF

PORK AND BLACK BEAN STEW

BEEF STIR-FRY

AMERICAN BISCUITS

QUICK CORN BREAD

THAI VEGETABLE CURRY

It may seem a stretch to make a curry with a fresh paste in half an hour, but it's perfectly possible and the flavour is fantastic. Obviously you can use shop-bought paste if you prefer. We've included Thai basil which you see in lots of supermarkets now, but don't worry too much if you don't have any – just use a mix of ordinary basil and coriander instead.

SERVES 4

1 tsp coconut or vegetable oil

2 shallots, thinly sliced

400ml reduced-fat coconut milk

200ml hot vegetable stock

2 Kaffir lime leaves, shredded

1 medium aubergine

200g butternut squash

200g green beans

1 large courgette

½ small cauliflower (about 200g)

juice of 1 lime

small bunch of coriander leaves

small bunch of Thai basil (optional)

flaked sea salt

freshly ground black pepper

Curry paste

1 red chilli

1 tbsp coriander stems

2 shallots

4 garlic cloves

10g fresh root ginger

2 lemongrass stalks or 1 tbsp lemongrass paste

1 tbsp galangal paste (optional)

1 tbsp soy sauce or tamari

½ tsp turmeric

First prepare the ingredients for the curry paste. Deseed the chilli if you want to decrease the heat. Roughly chop the chilli, coriander stems, shallots and garlic. Peel and chop the ginger. Remove the outer layers of the lemongrass stalks, if using, then roughly chop the soft, white centres.

Put all the paste ingredients into a food processor with some salt and pepper. Add a splash of water and blitz until fairly smooth.

Put the coconut or vegetable oil in a large saucepan. Add the shallots and cook them for a couple of minutes, then add the paste. Stir the paste for 2–3 minutes until it smells very aromatic, then pour in the coconut milk and vegetable stock. Add the lime leaves, season with salt and pepper and leave to simmer gently while you prepare the rest of the ingredients.

Cut the aubergine and butternut squash into fairly large chunks of about 3cm. Add them to the saucepan, cover the pan with a lid and simmer for 5 minutes. Meanwhile, trim the green beans, cut the courgette into chunks and separate the cauliflower into florets, cutting them in half if very large. Add these to the pan, then cover again and simmer for a further 5 minutes.

When all the vegetables are tender, add the lime juice. Taste the curry for seasoning and add more soy sauce or tamari if necessary. Serve sprinkled with coriander leaves and Thai basil leaves, if using.

170 calories per serving

BLACK-EYED PEAS AND GREENS

We love the food of the southern US and this is our version of a Cajun favourite – black-eyed peas and greens. We call 'em black-eyed beans over here but they're the same thing. We use spring greens instead of collard greens and haven't included any pork, although you could add a bit of bacon if you like – and you could use 10 grams of lard instead of the oil if you're not cooking for vegetarians. This is extra good served with corn bread so have a look at our recipe on page 311.

Heat the vegetable oil in a large saucepan or a flameproof casserole dish over a medium heat. Add the onion, celery and green pepper to the pan, turn the heat up high and stir for 5 minutes – the vegetables should be browning nicely by this point.

Sprinkle over the garlic powder and onion powder, if using, and the spices and herbs. Stir for a minute, and then add the beans. Pour over the vegetable stock and season with salt and pepper.

Bring to the boil, cover the pan, then turn down the heat and cook for 5 minutes. During this time, wash and shred the spring greens. Pile these on top of the beans – do not stir at this stage.

Turn the heat up again and cover. After 5 minutes the spring greens will have wilted down a little. Stir to combine with the rest of the ingredients and leave to simmer for a further 5 minutes. Serve with corn bread (see p.311).

Biker tip: If you'd like to freeze this dish, cook it up to the stage of adding the greens. After defrosting, reheat, add the greens and finish as above.

SERVES 4

1 tbsp vegetable oil

1 sweet white onion, diced

2 celery sticks, diced

1 green pepper, deseeded and diced

2 tsp garlic powder

1 tsp onion powder (optional)

1 tsp sweet smoked paprika

1 tsp ground cumin

½ tsp cayenne pepper

1 tsp dried oregano or mixed herbs

2 bay leaves

2 x 400g cans of black-eyed beans, drained and rinsed

500ml hot vegetable stock

200g spring greens

flaked sea salt

freshly ground black pepper

207 calories per serving

FISH CURRY

A hot and sour curry, this has a lovely fresh taste and is very simple to make. What's more, it's so low in calories that you can afford to treat yourself to a chapati as well if you fancy. If you're a curry fan you'll probably have some tamarind paste in your larder, but if not it's available in most supermarkets now and it does add a good tangy flavour.

SERVES 4

1 tbsp coconut or vegetable oil

2 onions, thinly sliced

3 garlic cloves, finely chopped

10g fresh root ginger, finely chopped

4 medium tomatoes or 400g canned chopped tomatoes

1 tbsp Kashmiri chilli powder or 2 tsp sweet paprika and 1 tsp cayenne

2 tsp ground cumin

1 tsp ground coriander

½ tsp turmeric

300ml hot fish stock or water

2 tbsp tamarind paste

juice of 1 lime

½ tsp caster sugar (optional)

600g skinned firm white fish fillets (hake or tilapia)

chopped fresh coriander

flaked sea salt

freshly ground black pepper

Heat the oil in a large shallow pan. You need one that has a lid and is wide enough to take all the fish in one layer. Add the onions and stir to coat them with the oil. Cover the pan and leave the onions over a low heat for 5 minutes to start softening while you prepare the garlic and ginger.

If using fresh tomatoes, remove the cores, then blitz them in a blender and set them aside.

Add the garlic and ginger to the onions and cook for a further minute. Sprinkle the spices into the pan and stir briefly to combine. Add the hot fish stock or water and season with salt and pepper. Simmer for 5 minutes, then add the tomatoes and tamarind paste. Bring the curry to the boil, then turn down the heat and leave to cook uncovered for another 5 minutes.

Add the lime juice, then taste the curry and if it seems a little too sour, add the sugar. Cut the fish into large chunks and sit these on top of the sauce, pressing them down very lightly. Cover the pan and cook for 3–4 minutes or until the fish is cooked through. Sprinkle with chopped coriander and serve at once.

226 calories per serving

FISH CRUMBLE

The only thing that's humble about this crumble is the calorie count! Cod, haddock or hake all work well and the smoked fish adds extra flavour. The creamy sauce contrasts brilliantly with the crunchy couscous topping – which we reckon is genius.

SERVES 4

600g skinless white fish fillets, cut into chunks

150g smoked haddock fillets, cut into chunks

low-cal oil spray

flaked sea salt

white pepper

Sauce

1 slice of onion

2 bay leaves

a few white peppercorns

50ml white wine

50ml milk

200ml half-fat crème fraîche

1 tsp plain flour

25g reduced-fat extra-mature Cheddar cheese

small bunch of parsley

Couscous topping

100g couscous

120ml just-boiled water

25g reduced-fat extra-mature Cheddar cheese

2 tsp olive oil

First put the oven on at 200°C/Fan 180°C/Gas 6 to heat up. Tip the couscous into a heatproof bowl and cover with the just-boiled water. Cover and leave the couscous to stand until all the water has been absorbed, then fluff it up with a fork.

For the sauce, put the onion and bay leaves in a saucepan with the peppercorns. Pour in the wine and milk, then stir in the crème fraîche. Put the pan over a low heat and whisk in the flour and cheese. When the sauce is well combined and the cheese has melted, leave to simmer gently for a couple of minutes, then add the fish. Continue to simmer for 3–4 minutes until the fish is just cooked through.

Finely chop the parsley and set aside 2 tablespoons. Stir the rest into the sauce. Spray a shallow ovenproof dish with oil. Spoon the fish and sauce into the dish and season with salt and white pepper.

Now add the topping. Mix the reserved chopped parsley with the couscous and spoon it over the sauce. Sprinkle the cheese on top – it will stop the couscous from crisping up too much – then drizzle over the olive oil. Bake the crumble in the preheated oven for about 10 minutes until everything is piping hot. Serve with some seasonal green vegetables.

388 calories per serving

CHICKEN AND PRAWN LAKSA

It might look like a lot to do here but the ingredients for the paste can be chopped roughly, as they will be blitzed, and the cooking is brief. You can use shop-bought laksa paste if you prefer, but the flavour won't be quite as punchy.

SERVES 4

1 tsp vegetable or coconut oil

500g skinless, boneless chicken breasts or thighs, diced

400ml can of reduced-fat coconut milk

600ml hot chicken stock

1–2 tbsp fish sauce

2 Kaffir lime leaves, finely shredded

1 carrot, cut into matchsticks

100g rice vermicelli

200g Chinese greens – any sort

100g bean sprouts

300g shelled raw prawns

juice of 1 lime

fresh coriander leaves

flaked sea salt

freshly ground black pepper

Laksa paste (or use a small jar of laksa paste)

2 lemongrass stalks, white centre only, roughly chopped

3 garlic cloves, roughly chopped

2 shallots, roughly chopped

10g fresh root ginger, chopped

2 Thai chillies, roughly chopped

1 tbsp puréed galangal (optional)

1 tsp shrimp paste

1 tsp ground cumin

1 tsp ground turmeric

428 calories per serving

If you're making your own paste, put all the ingredients in a food processor with a little water to get the mixture going and blitz until fairly smooth. Set aside.

Heat the oil in a large casserole dish or a wok. When it's shimmering, add the chicken and stir-fry for a minute or so just to seal and brown it all lightly, then turn down the heat and add the laksa paste. Stir for another couple of minutes, then pour in the coconut milk and stock.

Season with a tablespoon of the fish sauce, then add the lime leaves and the carrot and leave the laksa to simmer for 5 minutes. Taste and add the rest of the fish sauce if you think it needs it.

Cook the rice vermicelli according to the packet instructions, then drain.

Shred the greens and add them to the laksa. Cook for another couple of minutes, then add the bean sprouts, prawns and noodles. Simmer for a minute until the prawns have turned pink and opaque, then add the lime juice and more salt and pepper if you think it necessary. Serve sprinkled with plenty of fresh coriander.

TURKEY KEEMA PEAS

The trad keema pea dish is made with lamb, but our turkey mince version has far fewer calories and still tastes awesome. Best to get turkey thigh mince, rather than breast which will dry out more, or if you have a friendly local butcher, you could ask for minced chicken thighs which will also work well.

Heat the oil in a large lidded saucepan. Add the onion and fry it briskly over a high heat for a couple of minutes, stirring regularly, then add the garlic and ginger. Fry and stir for another minute.

Add the coriander leaves, curry powder and mince. Stir until the mince has browned slightly and is well coated with the spices. Add the bay leaf and pour in the tomatoes and the coconut milk. Season with salt and pepper.

Bring to the boil and cover the pan again. Simmer over a medium heat for 5 minutes, then take the lid off the pan and add the peas. Bring to the boil again, stir thoroughly, then turn down the heat and leave the mixture to simmer, uncovered, for another 10 minutes until the sauce has thickened. Serve sprinkled with plenty of coriander leaves. A small portion of rice or cauliflower rice alongside is nice.

SERVES 4

1 tsp coconut or vegetable oil

1 onion, finely chopped

2 garlic cloves, finely chopped

10g fresh root ginger, grated

small bunch of coriander, stems and leaves separated, stems finely chopped

1 tbsp mild curry powder

600g turkey thigh mince

1 bay leaf

400g can of chopped tomatoes

200ml reduced-fat coconut milk

250g petits pois, defrosted

flaked sea salt

freshly ground black pepper

270 calories per serving

STICKY CHICKEN DRUMSTICKS

There's nothing like a sticky drumstick. If anything, these are even better once they've cooled down, as the flavour develops, so they make a great treat to pop in your lunch box. Otherwise, serve them with a salad or any kind of veg you like. If you have any left over, strip off the meat and pack it into a wrap.

Preheat the oven to 180°C/Fan 160°C/Gas 4. Line a baking tray with baking parchment.

Using a sharp knife, slash the drumsticks through to the bone at intervals and put them on the baking tray. Bake them in the oven for 10 minutes.

Meanwhile, mix all the glaze ingredients together and season the mixture with salt and pepper. Remove the chicken drumsticks from the oven and brush them with half the glaze. Turn the oven up to 220°C/Fan 200°C/Gas 7 and bake the chicken for another 5 minutes.

Take the chicken out of the oven again and brush over the rest of the glaze, then cook for another 5 minutes. The chicken should be dark and sticky and completely cooked through.

SERVES 4

8 chicken drumsticks, skinned

Glaze

1 tbsp soy sauce

1 tbsp apricot jam

1 large garlic clove, crushed

5g fresh root ginger, grated

1 red chilli, deseeded and very finely chopped

1 tsp Chinese five-spice

flaked sea salt

freshly ground black pepper

223 calories per serving

CHICKEN CAULIFLOWER PILAF

Everyone loves a pilaf but the rice makes it quite a high-calorie dish. But if you use cauliflower instead of rice you get all that lovely comforting flavour and texture with far fewer cals. We're happy putting the whole spices into our pilaf and we're used to fishing them out as we eat, but if you're worried you could wrap them in a little bit of muslin and tie it at the top.

SERVES 4

500g skinless, boneless chicken breasts or thighs

large pinch of saffron

1 large onion, sliced into thin crescents

2 garlic cloves, finely chopped

5g fresh root ginger, finely chopped

1 tbsp vegetable or coconut oil

5 cardamom pods

2 x 3cm pieces of cinnamon stick

1 tsp cumin seeds

1 tsp fennel seeds (optional)

3 cloves

2 bay leaves

250ml hot chicken stock

1 medium cauliflower (about 750g)

flaked sea salt

freshly ground black pepper

To serve

1 tbsp pistachios

½ pomegranate

small bunch of coriander or parsley

274 calories per serving

First prepare the chicken. If using thighs, trim off any fat, then slice them thinly. If using chicken breasts, cut them into 2cm chunks. Put the saffron in a bowl with a little hot water and leave it to steep.

Heat the oil in a large, lidded frying pan or a shallow casserole dish. When the pan is hot, add the chicken. Fry the chicken for a minute, stirring constantly, until the pieces have seared, then add the onion, garlic and ginger and fry for another couple of minutes. Add the whole spices and the bay leaves.

Pour the stock and the saffron with its water into the pan, then season. Stir well, scraping up any brown bits from the base of the pan. Bring the stock to the boil, then leave to simmer while you prepare the cauliflower – this should take about 5 minutes. Cut up the cauliflower and blitz to the size of coarse breadcrumbs in a food processor – use the stalks as well as the florets.

When the liquid has reduced so it just coats the base of the pan and the chicken and onion are tender, remove the chicken and most of the onion with a slotted spoon and keep them warm. Add the cauliflower to the pan and stir so it is coated with the remaining liquid and spices – it should start to turn a light ochre in patches.

Cook over a medium heat for at least 5 minutes, stirring regularly, until the cauliflower is cooked through and the remaining liquid has evaporated. The cauliflower should be fluffy. Put half the chicken and onion back into the pan and stir it through the cauliflower, then add the rest on top.

While the cauliflower is cooking, lightly crush or chop the pistachios and remove the seeds from the pomegranate. Serve the pilaf sprinkled with the pistachios, pomegranate seeds and herbs.

PORK AND BLACK BEAN STEW

This is based on feijoada, a Brazilian favourite made with sausage, fatty pork ribs or shoulder and beans. The classic dish takes a long time to cook, but our version uses leaner cuts of meat that are cooked quickly and briefly so they don't dry out. It's still really rich and tasty though. Worth getting some good free-range pork for this if you can.

SERVES 4

300g lean pork steaks or tenderloin

75g smoked back bacon

1 large onion

2 garlic cloves

2 tsp olive oil

100g kabanos sausage

2 bay leaves

1 tsp dried oregano

stems from a small bunch of coriander, finely chopped

½ tsp chilli flakes (optional)

2 x 400g cans of black beans

300ml hot chicken stock

1 tbsp red wine vinegar

flaked sea salt (optional)

freshly ground black pepper

Salsa

1 tomato, finely diced

½ red pepper, finely diced

juice of 1 lime

½ tsp ground cumin

leaves from a small bunch of coriander, roughly chopped

flaked sea salt

freshly ground black pepper

Trim the pork of any fat and cut it into thin strips. Trim the bacon of any fat and dice. Peel and slice the onion into thin crescents and finely chop the garlic.

Heat half the olive oil in a large saucepan or a casserole dish. Add the bacon and onion and fry over a high heat for 3–4 minutes, then add the garlic, pork and sausage. Cook for another minute.

Add the bay leaves, oregano and coriander stems to the pan, together with the chilli flakes, if using. Pour in the black beans – with their liquid – then rinse out the tins with the chicken stock and pour this in too. Add the vinegar and season with pepper and salt, if needed – don't add salt at this stage if your black beans were in salted water.

Bring the stew to the boil, then turn down the heat and simmer for 10 minutes. The texture should be soupy but not runny.

While the pork and beans are cooking, make the salsa. Put the diced tomato and pepper in a bowl and add the lime juice and cumin. Season with salt and pepper and add the coriander leaves. Stir to combine, then leave to sit until the stew is ready.

Serve the pork and beans in bowls, with the salsa on the side to dollop on top.

380 calories per serving

BEEF STIR-FRY

Stir-fries are the speed dieter's best friend and this one completely fills the brief for a quick, healthy, low-cal meal. It's inspired by dishes we ate on our trip to Korea a couple of years ago. Just keep your portion of noodles down and fill up on all the lovely veg.

First cook the noodles, according to the packet instructions, then drain and toss them in the sesame oil. Trim the beef of any fat and cut the meat into thin strips.

Heat the vegetable oil in a wok. Add the red pepper and carrot and stir-fry for 3 minutes over a high heat. Add the spring onions and mushrooms and cook for another 2 minutes, then add the beef, garlic and root ginger. Continue to stir-fry until the beef is seared on all sides.

Trim the greens and slice them if the leaves are large. Pour the soy sauce and rice wine vinegar into the wok and add the greens, then cook over a slightly lower heat until the greens have wilted down. Add the noodles and warm them through.

Serve at once, sprinkled with sesame seeds.

SERVES 4

100g rice noodles

½ tsp sesame oil

300g steak (sirloin, flank, bavette or rump)

1 tbsp vegetable oil

1 red pepper, deseeded and sliced into strips

1 large carrot, cut into matchsticks

4 spring onions, cut into 1cm rounds

200g shiitake mushrooms

2 garlic cloves, finely chopped

5g fresh root ginger, finely chopped

large bag of pak choi or other Asian greens

2 tbsp soy sauce

1 tsp rice wine vinegar

1 tsp sesame seeds (white or black), to serve

283 calories per serving

AMERICAN BISCUITS

In the American Deep South, biscuits are essential for mopping up your grits and gravy. But they're not what we think of as biscuits in the UK – they're more like a kind of savoury scone and very good. Like corn bread, biscuits are made with a raising agent, not yeast, so are quick to do. Try these with our chicken casserole on page 323 – they make a great bit on the side.

MAKES 8

200g plain flour, plus extra for dusting

2 tsp baking powder

¼ tsp bicarbonate of soda

½ tsp salt

25g cold butter, diced

150ml buttermilk, plus extra for brushing

124 calories per biscuit

Preheat the oven to 220°C/Fan 200°C/Gas 7.

Put the plain flour in a food processor with the baking powder, bicarbonate of soda and salt. Add the butter, then process until the mixture resembles fine breadcrumbs. Pour in the buttermilk and process briefly again – the mixture should clump together and be slightly tacky.

Turn the dough out on to a lightly floured surface and knead a few times until it's well combined and smooth. Roll the dough out to a thickness of about 1.5cm and cut out rounds with a 6cm cookie cutter. Dip the cutter in flour each time so that it doesn't stick to the dough. You should get 8 biscuits.

Arrange the biscuits on a baking tray and brush them with a little more buttermilk. Bake them in the oven for 10–12 minutes. Best served while still warm.

QUICK CORN BREAD

Corn bread is a quick bread made with bicarb and baking powder instead of yeast, and is very popular in the States as a side dish. It's often served dripping with butter, but we like it just as it is with black-eyed peas and greens (see page 293). It's a perfect way of soaking up the juices. We've suggested greasing the pan with a little spray oil, but if you want a bit of extra flavour and you're not vegetarian, use a few grams of lard or pork dripping instead. We cut this into small squares – just try not to eat too many of them!

Preheat the oven to 220°C/Fan 200°C/Gas 7. Spray a 20 x 20cm brownie tin with low-cal oil and put it in the oven to heat up.

Put the cornmeal and flour in a large bowl with the baking powder, bicarbonate of soda and salt. Whisk the eggs and buttermilk together, then add them to the dry ingredients. Add the sweetcorn and jalapeños, if using, and mix thoroughly.

Remove the tin from the oven, then as quickly as you can, spread the batter evenly over the base of the tin. The easiest way to do this is with a palette knife. Put the tin back in the oven and bake the corn bread for 15 minutes until it's well risen and deep golden-brown. Remove the corn bread from the oven and allow it to cool a little before cutting it into about 25 squares.

MAKES 25 SMALL SQUARES

low-cal oil spray

250g medium-coarse cornmeal

100g plain flour

1 tbsp baking powder

¼ tsp bicarbonate of soda

½ tsp salt

2 large eggs

284ml carton of buttermilk

Extras (optional)

200g sweetcorn

25g jalapeño slices (from a jar)

67 calories per square

SLOW, SLOW, QUICK, QUICK, SLOW

SLOW-COOKER BARLEY AND VEGETABLE STEW

SLOW-COOKER CHICKEN TAGINE

POT-ROAST BEEF

PRESSURE-COOKER RISOTTO

QUICK CHICKEN CASSEROLE

LAMB CURRY, DHANSAK STYLE

VEGETABLE DHAL

PRESSURE-COOKER TOMATO SAUCE

POACHED PEARS

CHOCOLATE MUG CAKE

SLOW-COOKER BARLEY AND VEGETABLE STEW

It may seem strange to include slow-cooker recipes in a fast food cookbook, but there is method in our madness! It's simply a case of spending that half hour of food prep in the morning, instead of in the evening. Gremolata is a cheeky little Italian number, often used to garnish slow-cooked meat dishes. It's finely chopped garlic, parsley and lemon zest and is just right for adding a tang of freshness to this stew.

SERVES 4

10g dried mushrooms (optional)

1 onion, finely chopped

1 celery stick, finely chopped

1 red pepper, finely chopped

1 large carrot, diced

200g butternut squash or sweet potato, diced

3 garlic cloves, finely chopped

a few sprigs of rosemary

1 tsp dried oregano

150g pearl barley

1 litre hot vegetable stock

shavings of Parmesan cheese or a vegetarian alternative

flaked sea salt

freshly ground black pepper

Gremolata (optional)

small bunch of parsley, finely chopped

zest of 1 lemon

2 garlic cloves, finely chopped

If using the mushrooms, soak them in a small dish of warm water for a few minutes while you prepare the vegetables.

Put the vegetables in the slow cooker with the garlic, rosemary, oregano and barley. Season with salt and pepper, then pour over the stock. Add the dried mushrooms and their soaking water.

Put the lid on the slow cooker and leave to cook on low for about 5 hours. By this point the barley should be cooked through and plump and the vegetables should be tender but still holding their shape.

To make the gremolata, mix the parsley, lemon zest and garlic together. Serve the barley stew garnished with the gremolata, if using, and some shavings of cheese.

V ❄ *241 calories per serving*

SLOW-COOKER CHICKEN TAGINE

Tagines are not usually an option for a mid-week supper, as they take ages to cook. But pop everything in your slow cooker in the morning and you'll be rewarded with the magical aromas of Morocco when you get home and a perfectly cooked meal. Yum.

SERVES 4

1 onion, thinly sliced

2 garlic cloves, finely chopped

1 tbsp ground coriander

1 tbsp ground cumin

1 tbsp ground ginger

½ tsp cinnamon

¼ tsp ground cloves

zest and juice of 1 lemon

400g can of chickpeas, drained and rinsed

8 bone-in chicken thighs, skinned

8 dried apricots

25g pitted green olives

250ml hot chicken stock

flaked sea salt

freshly ground black pepper

Put the onion and garlic in the slow cooker and add all the spices and the lemon zest. Stir to mix everything together.

Add the chickpeas, then arrange the chicken thighs on top. Slice each apricot in half through the middle to create 2 thin pieces (rather than 2 semi-circles) and add them to the slow cooker with the olives. Season with salt and pepper and pour over the chicken stock.

Put the lid on and cook on low for 8 hours. Add the lemon juice towards the end of the cooking time.

Good served with cauliflower couscous or the regular kind, sprinkled with parsley.

❄ *355 calories per serving*

POT-ROAST BEEF

Okay, this one is a little more work than the other slow-cooker recipes but it's well worth it. As we've always said, cheaper cuts of meat such as chuck and silverside have the best flavour and this is a prime example. BTW, if you don't want to make your own bouquet garni, you can use a shop-bought one.

SERVES 6

1 tbsp plain flour

1 tsp mustard powder

1 tsp mixed herbs

1.2–1.5kg beef chuck or silverside, trimmed of fat

1 tbsp olive oil

1 onion, finely diced

2 carrots, finely diced

2 celery sticks, finely diced

2 garlic cloves, finely chopped

1 tbsp tomato purée

1 tbsp anchovy paste

200ml red wine

500ml hot beef stock

bouquet garni made of a sprig of thyme, 2 sprigs of parsley and 2 bay leaves

flaked sea salt

freshly ground black pepper

367 calories per serving

Sprinkle the plain flour over a plate and season it with salt and pepper. Add the mustard powder and herbs and mix thoroughly. Roll the beef in the flour mixture until it's completely covered, then pat off any excess.

Heat 1 teaspoon of the olive oil in a frying pan. Sear the beef on all sides – this will take at least 2–3 minutes on each side so while this is happening, prepare the vegetables and garlic.

When the beef is browned, remove it from the pan and set it aside. Put the remaining oil in the pan, add the vegetables and garlic and cook them over a high heat for several minutes until they're starting to take on some colour. Add the tomato purée and anchovy paste and stir for another minute or so to cook the purée.

Pour the red wine into the pan and allow it to bubble, scraping up any brown bits from the base of the pan. Pour the entire contents of the pan into the slow cooker and add the beef. Pour over the beef stock and tuck in the bouquet garni, then season with a little salt and pepper.

Cook at a low heat for 7–8 hours until the beef is very tender. When the meat is ready, remove it from the slow cooker. Strain the cooking liquid into a saucepan, reserving the vegetables, and boil it for a few minutes to reduce it to a thick gravy. Serve the beef in thick slices with the vegetables and gravy. Some greens make a good accompaniment.

PRESSURE-COOKER RISOTTO

Risotto is one of our favourite dishes but it usually means standing over the saucepan stirring and that's not always what you feel like after a hard day's work. The good news is that with a pressure cooker, you can have a perfect risotto in no time – and with very little stirring. If you don't have a pressure cooker, make this in the usual way, adding the stock a little at a time, but it will take more than half an hour.

Heat the olive oil and butter in the pressure cooker. Add the onion and cook it gently for 5 minutes, until it has started to soften, then add the garlic, courgette, lemon zest and rice. Continue to stir for a minute so the rice becomes well coated with the oil and butter.

Turn up the heat and pour the white wine into the pan. Allow it to bubble up for a minute or so until it has reduced, then pour in the stock. Season with salt and pepper.

Click the pressure cooker lid into place and leave it over a high heat until it comes up to pressure. Turn the heat down and leave to cook at high pressure for exactly 5 minutes, then fast release.

While the risotto is cooking, bring a kettle of water to the boil. Put the peas in a bowl and pour half the water over the peas to defrost them and pour the rest into a saucepan. Shred the greens and put them in the saucepan with the drained peas. Bring the water to the boil and cook the peas and greens for 2–3 minutes until they're cooked through but still a nice fresh green, then drain.

Put the pressure cooker over a low heat, with the lid off. Add the peas and greens to the pan together with the grated cheese. Beat until the cheese has melted and the risotto is creamy. Serve immediately.

SERVES 4

1 tsp olive oil

5g butter

1 onion, finely chopped

2 garlic cloves, finely chopped

1 large courgette, diced

1 tsp lemon zest

200g Arborio risotto rice

75ml white wine

400ml hot vegetable stock

100g frozen peas

100g chard, kale or spring greens

25g Parmesan cheese or a vegetarian alternative, grated

flaked sea salt

freshly ground black pepper

319 calories per serving

QUICK CHICKEN CASSEROLE

You can make a beautiful chicken casserole in less than half an hour in a pressure cooker, so for the impatient healthy eater, one of these bits of kit could be a welcome addition to your kitchen. We love this served with our American biscuits (see page 314) to mop up the lovely juices.

Cut the chicken thighs in half, or quarters if they're particularly large. Heat the olive oil in the pressure cooker, add the chicken thighs and cook them over a high heat for a couple of minutes or until seared all over. Remove them with a slotted spoon and set aside. Add the onion to the pan and cook for another few minutes.

Add the garlic, mushrooms and butternut squash and cook for another 2 minutes. Put the chicken back in the pressure cooker and sprinkle in the sage. Stir in the mustard and pour the white wine and chicken stock into the pan.

Season with salt and pepper, then click the lid into place and bring the cooker up to high pressure. Cook for 4 minutes at high pressure, then remove the pan from the heat and allow the pressure to drop naturally.

When the pressure has dropped, remove the lid, add the crème fraiche and simmer over a low heat until the sauce is slightly reduced. Sprinkle the casserole with parsley just before serving.

SERVES 4

500g skinless, boneless chicken thighs

1 tbsp olive oil

1 onion, thickly sliced

2 garlic cloves, finely chopped

200g button mushrooms, wiped clean

300g butternut squash, cut into chunks of about 3cm

1 tsp dried sage

1 tsp Dijon mustard

100ml white wine

100ml hot chicken stock

2 tbsp half-fat crème fraiche

2 tbsp finely chopped parsley

flaked sea salt

freshly ground black pepper

250 calories per serving

LAMB CURRY, DHANSAK STYLE

A curry like this usually needs to simmer for hours but you can make a great version in a pressure cooker. Be sure to heat the stock before you pour it in or you will slow things down. If you don't have all the spices, you can use a medium curry powder instead – about a tablespoon should do it. Nice with cauli rice instead of regular rice to keep the calories down.

SERVES 4

750g stewing lamb (leg or shoulder)

1 tbsp vegetable or coconut oil

1 onion, thickly sliced

3 garlic cloves, finely chopped

10g fresh root ginger, finely chopped

12 dried apricots

1 tbsp ground coriander

1 tsp ground cardamom

1 tsp turmeric

½ tsp ground cinnamon

½ tsp cayenne pepper

¼ tsp ground cloves

50g red lentils, rinsed

300ml hot chicken or lamb stock or water

juice of ½ lemon

fresh coriander, to serve

flaked sea salt

freshly ground black pepper

414 calories per serving

Trim any visible fat off the lamb and dice the meat into bite-sized pieces. Heat the oil in the pressure cooker. Add the lamb, onion, garlic and ginger and cook over a high heat for 2 minutes. Meanwhile, slice each apricot in half through the middle, so you end up with 2 thin pieces rather than semi-circles.

Sprinkle the spices over the lamb, then add the lentils and apricots. Pour in the hot stock and season with salt and pepper. Close the lid of the pressure cooker and cook over a high heat until it reaches pressure. Cook for 12 minutes at high pressure, then if you have time, let the pressure drop naturally – otherwise go for fast release.

When the pressure has dropped, remove the lid and stir in the lemon juice. Serve the curry sprinkled with fresh coriander.

VEGETABLE DHAL

This is not one of your dribbly dhals but a proper meal in itself, especially if served with some rice or flatbread. And we find it's even better cooked in a pressure cooker than in a regular pan. A green vegetable alongside is nice too.

SERVES 4

1 tbsp vegetable or coconut oil

1 onion, finely diced

2 garlic cloves, finely chopped

5cm fresh root ginger, grated

2 tbsp coriander stems, finely chopped

1 sweet potato, diced

1 tbsp curry powder

200g red lentils

500ml hot vegetable stock or water

400g can of chopped tomatoes

50g frozen spinach or 100g fresh spinach

flaked sea salt

freshly ground black pepper

To serve

a few green chillies, thinly sliced

a few coriander leaves, torn

lemon wedges

Heat the oil in the pressure cooker and add the onion. Cook it over a medium heat for 5 minutes until it's starting to take on some colour, then add the garlic, ginger, coriander stems, sweet potato and curry powder. Stir thoroughly for a minute or so until everything is well coated with the curry powder.

Add the red lentils, then pour the hot stock or water and the tomatoes into the pan. Season with salt and pepper and stir thoroughly again. Add the spinach – if using frozen spinach you can defrost it in hot water first, if you like, but you don't have to.

Click the lid into place and bring the cooker up to high pressure. Turn down the heat and cook the dhal at high pressure for 1 minute only, then remove from the heat and leave the pressure to drop naturally. The lentils will continue to cook during this time.

When the pressure has dropped, remove the lid and stir vigorously so everything is well combined. Garnish with the chillies and coriander and serve with lemon wedges to squeeze over the top.

V ❄ *315 calories per serving*

PRESSURE-COOKER TOMATO SAUCE

We like to make plenty of this and stash some away in the freezer for another day. A good tomato sauce usually needs a good hour to bubble and reduce, but you can make one in the pressure cooker in less than half the time. Great to serve with pasta or with some meatloaf or burgers.

Heat the olive oil in the pressure cooker and add the onion. Cook it over a medium to high heat for 5 minutes, stirring regularly, until it starts to colour around the edges.

Add the garlic and cook for another minute. Turn up the heat and pour in the white wine, then let it bubble furiously for a couple of minutes. Strip the leaves from the basil and add the stems to the pressure cooker, keeping the leaves aside. Sprinkle in the oregano, then pour the tomatoes into the pan and season with salt and black pepper.

Close the lid of the pressure cooker and bring it up to high pressure. Cook the sauce at high pressure for 10 minutes, then fast release. Leave the sauce to simmer, uncovered, for another 5 minutes to reduce a little. Shred the basil leaves and stir them in at the last minute.

SERVES 4

1 tbsp olive oil

1 onion, finely diced

3 garlic cloves, finely chopped

150ml white wine

small bunch of basil

1 tsp dried oregano

2 x 400g cans of chopped tomatoes

flaked sea salt

freshly ground black pepper

---

111 calories per serving   V

POACHED PEARS

Normally, poached pears take at least half hour to cook but in the pressure cooker they take six minutes. They're good to eat and make a reasonably healthy dessert, as you discard most of the sugar syrup they're cooked in. We've cut down the sugar in the syrup as much as we dare so it's best to use fairly sweet pears if you can find them. The amaretti biscuits add a lovely crunch and they're only 29 calories each.

Put the hot water and white wine in the pressure cooker with the sugar. Split the vanilla pod down the middle and add this too. Put the pan over a low heat and stir until the sugar has completely dissolved.

Put the lemon or lime juice into a large bowl and add cold water. Peel the pears, removing the cores from the base, and drop each one into the bowl of citrus water as you go – this stops the pears going brown.

When you have prepared all the pears, strain them and add them to the pressure cooker. Close the lid, bring the cooker up to high pressure, then turn down the heat and cook at high pressure for 6 minutes.

Fast release the pressure and open the lid. Remove the pears and let them cool down for a while before serving – they are best at room temperature.

Crumble the amaretti biscuits until they are the consistency of breadcrumbs. Serve the pears in individual bowls, with a little crème fraiche sprinkled with biscuit crumbs.

SERVES 6

500ml hot water

100ml white wine

100g caster sugar

1 vanilla pod

juice of ½ lemon or lime

6 ripe but firm pears

To serve

4 small amaretti biscuits

4 tbsp half-fat crème fraiche

176 calories per serving

CHOCOLATE MUG CAKE

For those moments when only cake will do, try our microwave wonders. We realise you might have to keep your lunch very low-cal if you're going to treat yourself to one of these but they're so quick and easy – and good – it could be worth it.

Put the plain flour, cocoa, espresso powder, baking powder and sugar in a bowl and whisk to remove any lumps.

Mix all the remaining ingredients, except the oil, together. Add them to the dry ingredients and stir thoroughly until smooth.

You need a mug that holds about 200ml and can go in the microwave. Spray it with low-cal oil, then pour in the cake batter.

Put the mug in the centre of your microwave and cook on high power for 1 minute only. Check to see if the cake is done – you want it to be cooked on top and slightly springy. If it's not quite ready, cook for another 15 seconds.

Delve in and eat the cake from the mug with perhaps a spoonful of half-fat crème fraiche.

SERVES 1

2 tbsp plain flour

1 tbsp cocoa

½ tsp instant espresso powder

¼ tsp baking powder

1 tbsp caster sugar

1 egg

1 tbsp low-fat yoghurt

10g butter, melted

2 tbsp milk

a few drops of vanilla extract

low-cal oil spray

half-fat crème fraiche, to serve

---

417 calories per cake
442 calories with a tablespoon
of half-fat crème fraiche

SPEEDY SWEETS

FAIRY CAKES

CRUNCHY OAT COOKIES

COCONUT AND CARROT MACAROONS

QUICK INDIVIDUAL CHEESECAKES

INSTANT SORBET

ICED BERRIES WITH WHITE CHOCOLATE SAUCE

GRILLED PINEAPPLE

RASPBERRY AND ORANGE SOUFFLÉS

QUICK RICE PUDDING

SWEET OMELETTE

BAKED BANANAS WITH CHOCOLATE RUM SAUCE

ZABAGLIONE

FAIRY CAKES

Cake for tea in half an hour? No problem. These little fairy cakes are lovely and light and so are fine just as they are, but we like to add the soft icing for an extra-special treat. Take one of these to work with you for that mid-afternoon snack attack.

MAKES 12

125g plain flour

1 tsp baking powder

50g butter, softened

75g caster sugar

grated zest of 1 orange

2 large eggs

2 tbsp orange juice

50ml 0% fat yoghurt

Icing

100g low-fat soft cream cheese

1 tbsp icing sugar or maple syrup

2 tbsp orange juice

1 tbsp grated orange zest

128 calories per cake

Preheat the oven to 180°C/Fan 160°C/Gas 4. Line a fairy cake tin with paper cases.

Put the flour and baking powder in a bowl and whisk to get rid of any lumps.

Put the butter, sugar and orange zest in a separate bowl and whisk or beat until light and fluffy. Add the eggs, one at a time, with a tablespoon of flour, beating lightly in between each addition. Add the rest of the flour, then beat in the orange juice and yoghurt. The mixture should have a dropping consistency.

Divide the mixture between the fairy cake cases – each should hold about a dessertspoonful. Bake the cakes in the oven for 12–15 minutes until they are well risen – they won't turn evenly brown because of the low amount of sugar so don't be tempted to overcook for colour. Put the cakes on a rack to cool while you make the icing.

Whisk together the cream cheese, icing sugar or maple syrup and orange juice until smooth. Swirl a little icing on top of each cake and sprinkle on a little orange zest.

CRUNCHY OAT COOKIES

Some shop-bought cereal bars are scarily high in calories so try these instead. At only 156 calories each, our cookies make a tasty little morsel with a cuppa. The oats fill you up and keep you going too.

MAKES ABOUT 16

100g plain flour
1 tsp baking powder
pinch of salt
200g porridge oats
75g raisins or chocolate chips
85g butter, softened
100g light brown sugar
1 egg

156 calories per cookie

Preheat the oven to 180°C/Fan 160°C/Gas 4.

Put the flour in a bowl with the baking powder and a pinch of salt. Whisk briefly to make sure there aren't any lumps, then stir in the porridge oats and the raisins or choc chips.

Put the butter and sugar in a separate bowl and whisk until very light and fluffy. Beat in the egg, then combine the butter mixture with the dry ingredients. Mix thoroughly.

Take tablespoons of the mixture, forming them into little balls about the size of a ping-pong ball and place them on a baking tray. Flatten them down a little so they aren't too thick in the middle.

Bake the cookies in the oven for 12–15 minutes until lightly coloured. Remove them from the oven and leave them to set on the baking tray for 3 minutes, before transferring them to a rack to cool.

COCONUT AND CARROT MACAROONS

These are not the trendy French macaroons, but the old-fashioned sort, like our mams used to bake. We've cut back the calories by adding carrot and less coconut so for once you can have your cake and eat it!

MAKES 12

2 egg whites at room temperature

pinch of salt

60g caster sugar

100g carrot, finely grated

100g desiccated coconut

1 tsp vanilla extract

1 tbsp cornflour or plain flour

❄ *84 calories per macaroon*

Preheat the oven to 180°C/Fan 160°C/Gas 4. Line a baking tray with baking parchment or use a non-stick baking tray.

Whisk the egg whites with a pinch of salt until they form soft peaks – this should only take a couple of minutes. Add all the sugar and continue to whisk until the mixture is shiny and full of air.

Squeeze out any excess liquid from the grated carrot and add it to the egg whites. Add the coconut and the vanilla extract, sift in the flour, then stir to mix everything together thoroughly. Be gentle so you don't lose all the air.

Put heaped tablespoons of the mixture at well-spaced intervals on the baking tray – you should get 12. Bake the macaroons in the oven for 15–20 minutes until golden brown. Remove them from the baking tray and leave them on a rack to cool.

QUICK INDIVIDUAL CHEESECAKES

If we were posh, we'd probably call this a deconstructed cheesecake. We're not, but it's still the speediest of puds and fits the bill when you crave a bit of something sweet. Match this with a low-cal main dish and you can have a two-course supper for around 500 cals. The mixture of gingery biscuit crumbs with the mango and passion fruit is ace, but you could try plain biscuits and top with berries and a dash of lemon juice. Or you could use ginger biscuits. Up to you.

Put the biscuits in a plastic bag and bash them into fairly fine crumbs – or just blitz them in a food processor. You can leave a few little chunks if you like. Add the ground ginger and stir, then divide the mixture between 4 serving glasses or bowls.

Peel the mango and cut the flesh into fairly small dice. Cut the passion fruit in half and scoop out the flesh. Mix it with the mango and set aside.

Put the cream cheese or quark in a bowl and add the lime zest and juice. Mix thoroughly until smooth, then add the crème fraiche and icing sugar.

Add some of the cream cheese and lime mixture to each serving of biscuit crumbs, spreading it as evenly as you can, then top with some of the mango and passion fruit. Chill the little beauties until you are ready to serve.

SERVES 4

4 digestive biscuits

½ tsp ground ginger

1 large ripe mango

1 passion fruit

150g low-fat cream cheese or quark

zest and juice of 1 lime

150g half-fat crème fraiche

2 tbsp icing sugar

218 calories per serving

INSTANT SORBET

If you have some fruit in the freezer and you want a pud with very little effort, this is your answer – instant good karma. You can use almost any kind of fruit but those with lots of seeds might be a bit gritty. Strawberries, grapes and pitted cherries are all good and some supermarkets sell packs of frozen tropical fruits, such as pineapple, mango and papaya, which also work well.

Take the fruit out of the freezer about 20 minutes before you want to use it. The berries or pieces need to start softening around the edges without completely defrosting.

While the fruit is softening, put the caster sugar in a saucepan with 30ml of water and the lime juice. Simmer over a low heat until the sugar has dissolved, stirring regularly, then leave to cool.

Put the fruit into a blender with the syrup. Blitz until the mixture is fairly smooth, pressing it down at the sides frequently. Add the ice cubes and blitz again until the mixture is smooth and thick.

Serve immediately or decant the sorbet into a container and put it into the freezer.

SERVES 4

450g frozen fruit, such as seedless grapes, pitted cherries, strawberries

30g caster sugar

juice from 1 lime

6 large ice cubes

87 calories per serving

ICED BERRIES WITH WHITE CHOCOLATE SAUCE

Simplicity itself but highly pleasurable, this seems too naughty for words but it isn't that high in calories. The contrast between the cold, frosty berries and the hot creamy sauce is beyond delicious and will satisfy your chocolate cravings.

SERVES 4

400g mixed berries, such as strawberries, raspberries, blueberries, blackberries

White chocolate sauce

50g white chocolate

75ml single cream

1 coffee bean (optional)

1 tsp vodka (optional)

139 calories per serving

Pick over the berries and discard any damaged ones. Hull the strawberries, if using. Spread the berries out on a baking tray and put them in the freezer for 20 minutes – the berries won't freeze in this time, but they will frost nicely.

Just before you take the berries out of the freezer, make the sauce. Break the chocolate into a saucepan and pour over the cream. Add the coffee bean if you have one – it won't add a coffee flavour but it will add depth to the white chocolate. Pour in the vodka, if using.

Heat the sauce over a gently heat, stirring constantly. When the chocolate has melted, whisk the sauce vigorously for a minute or so.

Remove the berries from the freezer and put them in glass bowls, handling them as little as possible. Pour over the hot sauce and serve right away.

GRILLED PINEAPPLE

If you're really in a hurry, you can buy pineapple ready cored and cut up. Otherwise it's no trouble to peel and core it yourself and the rest of the recipe takes minutes. This is one of our favourite desserts when we're trying to shed some timber. Tropically fantastic.

SERVES 4

8 wedges of peeled and cored pineapple (about 400g)

juice of 1 lime

1 tbsp maple syrup or runny honey

1 tsp ground ginger

1 tbsp rum (optional)

4 tbsp yoghurt or half-fat crème fraiche

92 calories per serving (2 wedges)

Heat a griddle until it's very hot. This will take at least 5 minutes over a high heat. Put the wedges of pineapple in a bowl.

While the griddle is heating, whisk the lime juice with the maple syrup or honey, ground ginger and rum, if using, in a small jug. Pour this over the pineapple and mix thoroughly so all the wedges are well coated – it's best to do this with your hands.

Remove the wedges of pineapple from the bowl, draining off and reserving any excess juices, and place them on the hot griddle. Grill for 2–3 minutes on each side until the pineapple is heated through and is marked with char lines.

Serve with yoghurt or crème fraiche and pour over any reserved juices.

RASPBERRY AND ORANGE SOUFFLÉS

Lots of people are scared of soufflés but they really aren't that difficult and they are quick to make. Try your hand at these and you'll be surprised how easy they are – and posh enough to serve at a Downton Abbey dinner do. If you're feeling extra indulgent you could use a couple of tablespoons of orange liqueur instead of the orange juice.

SERVES 4

low-cal oil spray or 2g butter, melted

120g fresh raspberries

2 large eggs

35g caster sugar

1 tsp cornflour

zest of ½ orange, plus extra to garnish

2 tbsp orange juice

1 tsp icing sugar, to dust

105 calories per serving

Preheat the oven to 170°C/Fan 150°C/Gas 3½ and put a baking tray in the oven to heat up.

Spray the insides of 4 small ramekins with low-cal oil spray or brush them with a tiny amount of melted butter. Put a few raspberries in the base of each ramekin.

Separate the eggs. Whisk the egg whites in a bowl until they form stiff peaks, then add a tablespoon of the sugar and whisk again until glossy.

Whisk the egg yolks in a separate bowl with the remaining sugar, the cornflour, orange zest and orange juice. Add a tablespoon of the egg whites to the egg yolk mixture and fold it in, then fold in the rest of the egg whites. Do this as lightly as possible, but make sure the mixture is well combined – you don't want flecks of egg white running through it.

Divide the mixture between the ramekins, piling it up high, then run your finger round the rim. This will help the soufflés rise evenly.

Place the ramekins on the baking tray and cook the soufflés in the preheated oven for 10–12 minutes until they are lightly golden and well risen. Dust with icing sugar and scatter over the orange zest, then serve immediately.

QUICK RICE PUDDING

Fancy a pud for your tea? Team this with one of our soups as a first course and you've got a really comforting but still healthy meal, with a reasonable calorie total. We both remember our mams making rice pudding and leaving it to cook in a low oven for hours. In fact, you can cook a brilliant rice pud on top of the stove in half an hour. And for something really special, make this luxurious raisin sauce as well.

Put the rice in a medium saucepan and pour over the milk, single cream and vanilla extract. Bring to the boil, then immediately turn the heat down to something between a boil and a simmer.

Cook the rice, stirring very regularly, for 20–25 minutes. By the end of this time the rice should be plumped up and tender, and the liquid well reduced.

Add the sugar and stir until it has dissolved, then remove the pan from the heat. The pudding will thicken more as it cools so don't leave it too long.

While the rice is cooking, make the sauce, if serving. Put the raisins in a small saucepan with the Marsala and lemon zest. Bring to the boil and continue to boil until the Marsala has reduced by half. Add the sugar, then turn down the heat and stir until the sugar has dissolved. Simmer until the liquid has turned syrupy. Serve the sauce with the rice pudding.

SERVES 4

125g short-grain pudding rice

600ml whole milk

50ml single cream

1 tsp vanilla extract

2 tbsp light brown soft sugar

Marsala raisin sauce (optional)

50g raisins

75ml sweet Marsala wine

zest of ½ lemon

1 tbsp light brown soft sugar

266 calories per serving
341 calories per serving (with sauce)

SWEET OMELETTE

Everyone knows that an omelette is the perfect quick meal, but a sweet omelette also makes a good speedy pudding – a little bit of eggstacy! You can use any fruit you like for the compote or just serve the omelette with fresh fruit and crème fraiche. This makes one big omelette to share between two, but you could also make individual ones in smaller pans. Arrowroot is a bit like cornflour and is used for thickening sauces and the like. It's available in supermarkets.

First make the compote. Put the blueberries or cherries in a saucepan with the sugar, lime zest and juice and add 2 tablespoons of water. Cook gently until the sugar has dissolved and the blueberries have softened. Mix the arrowroot with a little cold water in a small bowl and stir until you have a completely smooth paste. Add this to the blueberries and stir until the sauce has thickened. Keep the compote warm while you make the omelette. Put the grill on at its highest setting to heat up.

Break the eggs into a bowl and add the sugar. Using a hand-held electric whisk, beat the eggs and sugar until they are full of air and you can trail a ribbon across the surface – this should take 3–4 minutes.

Spray a non-stick frying pan with low-cal oil or melt the tiniest amount of butter and wipe it over the base of the pan so it is entirely covered. Tip the egg mixture into the frying pan, using a palette knife to make sure it covers the base evenly.

Cook the omelette over a medium heat for no longer than 2 minutes. To check the underside, lift up an edge – it should be just set and a very light golden brown. Be very careful when you do this, as the omelette is very delicate at this stage.

Put the pan under the hot grill and cook the omelette until the top is also set and starting to brown very lightly. This will only take a couple of minutes so watch the omelette constantly to make sure you don't overcook it.

Remove the pan from the grill and gently fold the omelette in half, then cut it down the middle. Serve with the fruit compote and a little crème fraiche.

SERVES 2

2 large eggs

2 tsp caster sugar

low-cal oil spray or 2g butter

2 dessertspoons crème fraiche, to serve

Quick fruit compote

150g blueberries or pitted black cherries (canned or jarred are fine)

2 tsp caster sugar

zest and juice of ½ lime

1 tsp arrowroot

237 calories per serving

BAKED BANANAS WITH CHOCOLATE RUM SAUCE

Well – chocolate rum sauce is not something you expect to find in a diet book, but we like to look after you all, and we do love something sweet from time to time. In fact, the sauce is made with a small amount of dark chocolate and isn't as calorific as it sounds, although it still tastes wicked!

SERVES 4

1 tsp butter

4 bananas

1 tbsp demerara sugar

1 tbsp rum

Chocolate rum sauce

50g dark chocolate

50ml milk

1 tbsp soft light brown sugar

1 tbsp rum

214 calories per serving

Preheat the oven to 200°C/Fan 180°C/Gas 6. Line a baking tray with a piece of foil that's big enough to overlap the edges of the tray slightly. Rub the foil with half the butter.

Peel the bananas and cut each one in half lengthways. Arrange the bananas on the foil and sprinkle over the sugar and rum. Take another piece of foil and rub it with the rest of the butter. Put the foil, butter-side down, over the bananas and crimp the edges of the pieces of foil together. Bake the bananas in the oven for 20 minutes.

Meanwhile, make the sauce. Break up the chocolate and put it in a saucepan with the milk, sugar and rum. Heat gently until the chocolate has melted, then whisk the sauce quite vigorously to make sure everything has combined properly. Remove the pan from the heat – the sauce will thicken slightly as it cools.

Take the bananas out of the oven and serve them on plates or in bowls. Drizzle the bananas with spoonfuls of the chocolate sauce.

ZABAGLIONE

Not a pudding for the little ones, as this tastes quite alcoholic. Great treat though and you could add some spices to make a festive Christmas dish. You need a heatproof bowl that fits nicely over a saucepan when making this.

SERVES 4

4 egg yolks

50g caster sugar

50g sweet Marsala wine

½ tsp vanilla extract

1 thinly pared strip of orange or lemon zest, plus extra to garnish

---

130 calories per serving

Bring a kettle of water to the boil. Half fill a saucepan with boiled water and set it over a medium heat to simmer.

Put the egg yolks, sugar, Marsala, vanilla extract and orange or lemon zest into a heatproof bowl that fits over the pan. Set the bowl over the saucepan, making sure that the bottom of the bowl isn't touching the simmering water.

Using a hand-held electric whisk, beat the contents of the bowl until they're light and fluffy and the whisk leaves a trail along the surface. This should take between 5 and 10 minutes. Take the pan off the heat and carefully remove the bowl. Take out the zest.

Divide the zabaglione between 4 small cups or serving glasses, garnish with orange or lemon zest and serve warm or cool.

INDEX

YOUR DIETER STORIES

'I was bored of never having takeaways and just eating salad. I bought the cookbook and have cooked everything in it … and guess what! I have lost a total of 13 stone to date.'
Joanne Richards

'The book is amazing and I have cooked from it on most days. Wow what a transformation! The biggest success is my husband who has lost 22 kgs! I am so incredibly proud of him.'
Nichola Beard

'I have lost 5 stone – so 70 lbs lighter … thanks to the Hairy Dieters cookbook for helping me immensely with some great food and making it not seem too much like a diet!'
Chris Rolph

'Don't just try the odd recipe; throw yourself into the book, work your shopping list around it and reap the rewards. I did it and have been absolutely blown away by the results. Not only have I felt that I've eaten more but I have lost 50 lbs.'
Paul Gilks

'We have been using the book now for 3 months. G has lost 5 stone and I have lost just over 3 stone. We both feel great and are not bored with the food at all.'
Tracy Edwards

'I bought the Hairy Dieters cookbook and I have cooked quite a few of the recipes – the whole family enjoy them! So far I have lost 45 lbs in 12 weeks! My bad back is improving too! Thanks Bikers!'
Sally Thomas

'Finally an eating profile (not diet) that I can get inspired enough to try. I'm exactly who you are aiming this at: 44, too fat, and with young kids who I want to play with as they grow up – but I love my food. So your journey has been exactly what I needed – honest, real, and above all, tasty!'
Iain Murray

'It's so nice to be able to eat delicious food and still lose weight. We always recommend your recipes to all our friends!'
Kerry and Martin

ACKNOWLEDGEMENTS

We love writing our books but we couldn't do it without all the wonderful help and support from Team Hairy.

We'd like to thank Catherine Phipps for her fantastic help and advice on the recipes, and Professor Ashley Adamson and Dr Suzana Almoosawi of the Institute of Health & Society and Human Nutrition Research Centre, Newcastle University, for their guidance on nutrition and for answering all our crazy questions.

Thanks to Andrew Hayes-Watkins who took all the photographs and always makes everything look so tempting and beautiful. We're eternally grateful to Lisa Harrison, Anna Burges-Lumsden and their assistants for preparing all the food so superbly for the pictures, and to Loulou Clark and Polly Webb-Wilson for providing all the plates and pans.

Thanks to Loulou Clark and Abi Hartshorne for the design, to Andy Bowden for his technical assistance and to creative director Lucie Stericker. Amanda Harris, our fabulous publisher, continues to give us huge support and encouragement and thank you too to Jinny Johnson, our editor, for helping us string the words together.

As always we would like to express our appreciation to all at James Grant Management who are always there for us. Big hugs to Nicola Ibison, Holly Pye, Natalie Zietcer, Tessa Findlay, Eugenie Furniss, Rowan Lawton and Sarah Hart – you're the best and we can't thank you enough. We'd also like to thank the Optomen team who worked so hard on the original Hairy Dieters television series.

Last but not least, we'd like to thank our Diet Club members for all their ideas and feedback – we've learned that dieting need never be boring. We love you all.

And don't miss the fantastic recipes in our other Hairy Dieters books!!

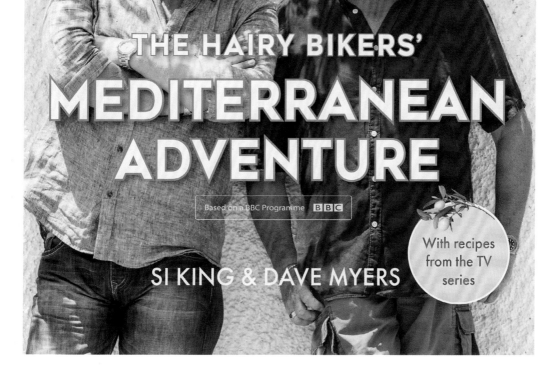

150 easy and tasty recipes to cook at home

THE HAIRY BIKERS'

MEDITERRANEAN
ADVENTURE

Based on a BBC Programme **BBC**

With recipes from the TV series

SI KING & DAVE MYERS

Out now!

We'd like to dedicate this book to our families, to Ashley Adamson, Roy Taylor and their teams at Newcastle University who put us on the right path, and to all the lovely staff at the Royal Victoria Infirmary in Newcastle for helping us both so much when Si was poorly.

Si & Dave x

The Hairy Dieters: Good Eating first published in 2014 by Weidenfeld & Nicolson
The Hairy Dieters: Fast Food first published in 2016 by Orion
This edition published in 2017 by Seven Dials, all imprints of the Orion Publishing Group Ltd
Carmelite House, 50 Victoria Embankment, London EC4Y 0DZ
An Hachette UK Company

A CIP catalogue record for this book is available from the British Library.

ISBN: 978 1 407 25101 1

Photographer: Andrew Hayes-Watkins
Food director: Catherine Phipps
Food stylists: Anna Burges-Lumsden, Lisa Harrison
Food team: Phil Wells, Lucy O'Reilly, Jane Brown, Anna McManus
Food stylist's assistants: Lou Kenny, Jane Brown
Design and art direction: Abi Hartshorne, Loulou Clark
Prop stylists: Loulou Clark, Polly Webb-Wilson
Technical artworker: Andy Bowden
Food and recipe consultant: Justine Pattison
Editor: Jinny Johnson
Proofreader: Elise See-Tai
Indexer: Vicki Robinson

Nutritional advice from Professor Ashley Adamson and Dr Suzana Almoosawi, Institute of Health & Society and Human Nutrition Research Centre, Newcastle University.

Nutritional analysis calculated by:
Fiona Hunter, Bsc (Hons) Nutrition, Dip Dietetics

Printed and bound in China

The Orion Publishing Group's policy is to use papers that are natural, renewable and recyclable and made from wood grown in sustainable forests. The logging and manufacturing processes are expected to conform to the environmental regulations of the country of origin.
www.orionbooks.co.uk